LISTEN to the OLD

Published by Maximilian Press
920 So. Battlefield Blvd., Suite 100
Chesapeake, Virginia 23322 USA

www.maximilianpressbookpublishers.com

757-482-2273

Maximilian Press Publishers and colophon
are registered trademarks of
Maximilian Press Publishers

For information about special discounts for bulk purchases,
please contact Maximilian Press Special Sales:
1-757-482-2273 or
E-mail:mpbp@maximilianpressbookpublishers.com

Composition and Format by M. Middleton
Cover design by M. Middleton
First printing: 2010

10 09 08 07 06 05 04 03 02 01
ISBN: 978-1-930211-98-8

This book has been composed in Baskerville Old Face.
The paper used in this publication meets the minimum
requirements of ANSI/NISO Z39.48-1992 (R1997)

LISTEN to the OLD

by Kathleen S. Blanchard   4. 14. 10

To Lynne Berg,
a talented and uniquely
driven person who
uses all the resources
at her disposal
to make our world
a happier and more
beautiful place for
the old.
God bless you,
Kathleen

CONTENTS

INTRODUCTION

This book is dedicated to all the old people who were kind enough to tell me their stories. This slim volume is loosely based on their stories; stories I have been fortunate enough to have heard, and heard them only because I listened. I listened to the old.

I have a sepia colored, 100 year old photograph of my Grandma's family that I keep close at hand. Grandma was between 10 and 12 years old in the photo, and in those days, photographs were pretty much staged and carefully posed events in middle class families. In this one, all the family members, Grandma, her Mother, Father and two Brothers were all in their best clothes, and Grandma had a large, white, floppy bow holding back her braided hair. What was most interesting to me in this formal, posed photograph was the inclusion of the family dog in the familial portrait. He, too, was proudly posing, and like the family, looking straight into the camera. There must be a story here. Seeing the dog with them, I thought my Great-Grandmother must have been a pretty nice lady to have taken him to the studio and included him in the portrait, too.

I began listening to the old when I was very young. Sixty years ago we had no television, and the relatives "in charge" did not suffer hearing, "I'm bored." In our family those words never passed from our lips. Children were cherished, but expected help: setting the table, washing the dishes, vacuuming rugs, ironing clothes (even tea towels and underwear), moving furniture so the floors beneath could be cleaned, burning trash, watching over younger siblings (even suffering the indignity of sitting in the playpen with them to amuse them), watching for the ice man, the milkman, the Jewel Tea man, and the delivery man from Hudson's Department store, making beds, running errands to the corner store, keeping one's room clean and straight, and keeping quiet when the adults were talking. Listening to the adults after your chores gave you a respite, and you did keep quiet. It was amazing what you learned about your family history, and, of course, you didn't want to interrupt. If you did, you may have been told to go outside and play, or worse yet, be given more chores to do to be rid of you while the adults got into the "juicy" stuff. My relatives had a secret weapon, though, to keep their conversations confidential. They often spoke Finnish. I'd watch them look directly at me, go off into agitated Finnish, pause, mention my name clearly, and continue on. I tried very hard to learn Finnish from my Grandma so that I'd be in on whatever they were saying about me. Grandma gave me a few phrases, but I could tell she was more interested in telling me some stories about her childhood, or sending me outside with a cookie so the house we had just cleaned would stay that way. We loved each other dearly, but my learning Finnish was not her priority. She told me stories about growing up in Finland; about the cow her grandmother had named "Lion" that could only be milked by her Grandmother; about the disheveled and bruised gypsies who came to her grandmother's door obviously attacked and assaulted by something bigger than any of them; about how her grandmother took one look at them and proclaimed, "You tried to milk 'Lion' didn't you?"; about lying on the hillside to watch the adults dancing and reveling during the midnight sun festival; about skiing to school in the winter; later, when she came to America; about hearing the explosions in New York when the Brooklyn shipyard was sabotaged during World War I; and about the rides Grandpa gave me in his old Hudson during World War II using his precious gas ration ticket to fuel the rides. I listened, and I could picture all the scenes in her stories, and because they related to me, they were even better than any radio program and later, any television show.

From this beginning, I developed a knack of listening to stories told by old people. After I married, a landlady told me of her life at the turn of the (previous) century, about the long, long, political speeches they had to endure before they could eat the fried chicken and strawberry cakes and pies; about practicing her spelling words with her mother while they washed the dishes; about working in her father's small dry goods store; about not marrying young but living with her sister and their parents until the parents died; about how she eventually married in her fifties and how her sister remained a spinster; about the man she married who was, as a young man, considered unacceptable and "wild" by her parents, and that she was to have nothing to do with him; about how this "wild" man changed and matured to own a plumbing business, married her and raised orchids with special grow lights in their basement.

When my husband served as a naval officer, maintenance men from the base who often came into our navy housing to fix plumbing and appliances, told me stories about their childhood; about digging up hibernating snakes, balled up and buried in the earth for the winter; about giggling and bringing these frozen snake balls in the house, thawing them out and playing with them; about their Mother coming into the room, seeing the wiggling, sleepy snakes and screaming; about being beaten with a belt (after the snakes were safely deposited back in the hole outside), first by their Mother and then by their Father; about their father keeping a pet King snake in their dairy barn to catch and eat rats and mice; about their Father capturing a baby King snake in the woods when the old one died, and about his Father taming his King snake to the point that it would drink from a saucer of milk, warm from the cow.

When I became the Coordinator for "Meals on Wheels," older, church volunteers and the recipients of "Meals on Wheels" told me stories of their growing up and courting. One especially stuck with me about two sisters who declared to their beaus that they could not marry them because they would never leave their widowed Mother; about the arrangement they all made to live in Mother's big house; about how the two couples lived compatibly with the Mother until she died; about how each couple had children; about how there was no question that they would all continue to live together; and how the only ones who left the house were the grown children or the spouses of the two couples as they died.

When my professional career expanded to actual case work with the old, I was able to devote significant time to listening to the old to help develop a care plan of benefits and programs to assist them. My special thanks go out to my first supervisor, Lynne Keating, who granted me the latitude to provide "friendly visiting" to lonely old people (Yes, that was a bona-fide service thirty years ago.), enabling them to trust me and to find viable solutions for them. Thanks are given to my creative coworkers, Rita Hassell and Joyce Moore, who before "heating and fuel" programs enlisted me with a borrowed truck to pick up cut wood from a client's felled tree, and carry it to another client who was cold and had no fuel for her wood stove. I can still see the three of us in my mind's eye, Joyce and I in our jeans and boots, and Rita in her high heels, carrying, stacking and unloading wood. I can't exactly remember what we called that particular service or exactly how we recorded it. The lady who was cold really didn't care, but was awfully glad we came with the wood. One of my favorite coworkers back then was Florence Swinton. She was "old" (over 60) herself, didn't much care for paperwork, but had unique solutions for lonely, stay at home, low income old people with chronic health conditions. Florence would beg the City Sheriff to let her have a Sheriff's van driven by a deputy. She would load the van with old people, and have the Sheriff's deputy carry the lot to Ahoskie, North Carolina, or some other "exotic" spot, to pick peaches, gather eggs from hen houses, and shop for towels and seconds in outlets. Those old people used muscles they didn't even know they had. Some even climbed trees, and they laughed and laughed. Florence won the "Good Samaritan Award" from her city one year for her encouragement and good deeds for these old people. She deserved it. Later, computers came in and the services became more strictly defined and documented. Florence said it was time to retire, and she did. She was sorely missed by us and her very sad clients.

I advanced in my career, first supervising my coworkers, and later supervising five departments and 38 contracts. I want to give special thanks to the Executive Director at that time, Kathleen Donoghue, who supported me as I adopted and implemented a management style recognizing our people as our greatest organizational asset. Our people were nurtured, guided, supported and applauded in their work with the old. Without listening to the old, there would be no organization, and there would be no reason to come to work.

Lastly, I must thank and give my eternal gratitude to my mother, Ida Regina Licht, and my husband, James Joseph Blanchard, who encouraged me and stood by me through low and high times. I love them dearly, and without their constant support, this book would have been impossible.

VIRGIL

Ohio was a long time ago.

I was born and lived in a small town with a common sense mentality. Honor your parents. Help your neighbor. Be true to your word. Somehow it seemed to work.

When I was twenty-one, I served with Dad on the "Dole Board." There were no handouts then, no welfare. If you needed to be put on the "dole," you needed to explain why you were in your predicament. Every month, in order to receive more assistance, you had to explain why you were still in that predicament. It seemed reasonable, and it worked.

The "Dole Board" had plenty of empathy, but no "bleeding hearts." Honesty, help and personal responsibility… that was the motto.

We were all living through the Depression. Everyone had some kind of sad story to tell. A sense of pride made most hang back from appearing before the Dole Board.

Dad and I were Masons. He bought me my Mason ring. I was proud of it, and proud of being part of it with Dad.

I played football, played pretty well, too. I was lucky, lucky enough to receive a football scholarship to college. I studied hard, hard enough to almost become a doctor. One year before my M.D., my number came up and Uncle Sam invited me to join the Army. War was going on, the big one, WW II. Uncle Sam said with my training I was smart enough then to become a Registered Nurse. Made me

1

an officer, and a nurse. I could fly, too. My uncle, Dad's brother, flew bi-planes in the "Great War." No parachutes then. If you were shot down then, you died. After livin' through all that, he made his living as a barn-stormin', stunt flyer in the 20's and 30's. People paid to take rides with him, too. He taught me to fly when I was twelve. He said I was a natural. I learned all his rolls and climbs and stunts. He was right proud of me. So with all that, Uncle Sam made me not only an Officer and a Registered Nurse, but a flying Registered Nurse.

I left Ohio for boot camp, flight training and the Pacific Theater of the War. Ohio never looked like this. Islands. Islands so small they didn't even show up as a dot on big maps. Beaches, white sandy beaches, palm trees and exotic fruits we'd only read about in Ohio. The sea was blue-green with white foam on top of the waves. The ocean crashing and pounding at our feet seemed to go on forever.

My home-base in the Philippines was peopled by small, smiling, happy people. They seemed to be happy that we came there. They knew about Pearl Harbor. They knew about the Japs. My work was intense at first. I had to learn all the names and all the locations of the islands. I had to learn about China, too. Rumors were that the Japanese had camps in China. We didn't know exactly where they were or what they did in those camps, but we heard rumors about them, and none of it was good. But, that was a whole 'nother world to learn about, and eventually, I would know exactly what happened in those camps.

Life was strangely routine in the Philippines. The Japanese didn't yet have the forces to get us. We'd fly out. Fly back with supplies, messages and wounded from the far off islands. Fly back to the safety of the Philippines. We'd wash, eat, drink, smoke, laugh and rest. Next day we'd fly out. Fly back with supplies, messages and wounded. Fly back into the safety of the Philippines. By and by, I met a beautiful nurse. God, she was gorgeous! Came from Georgia. I called her my Georgia Peach. I don't know why, but she agreed to marry me. I married her as fast as I could find a chaplain.

Life almost seemed "Ohio" there. I'd fly out. Fly back with supplies, messages and wounded. Fly back into the safety of the Philippines, and my Georgia peach. We had two babies. I'd fly out. Fly back with supplies, messages and wounded. I'd fly out and fly back to the love of my life, my Georgia Peach, and the noise and laughter of our two babies. Life was curiously routine and predictable on the base in the Philippines.

Rumors, then messages, told us that the Japanese were getting closer. They'd taken small islands and were working their way to the Philippines. The big General said it was time to evacuate the base. The pilots were to take their planes and fly away. The pilots were afraid, not for themselves, we would be safe. We could take the planes and ourselves to an Allied base. What about our families? What about our women? What about our children? What about our babies? The big General promised he would evacuate them on the ship we saw anchored off shore. He pointed to it. "See the ship in the harbor? That ship will carry your women, children and babies to safety. No harm will come to them. I promise." We pilots cried as we left. We kissed our wives, our children and our babies "good-bye." We were confident that we would meet again, soon, very soon. No harm would come to them. The ship would transport the women, children and babies to a safe Allied harbor. The General promised, so we flew out. We flew our planes out of harm's way, away from the Philippines and everyone we loved.

The big General had the ship loaded, all right, but not with our families. He had his family, his staff, their families, and all their stuff sent out on whaleboats to the ship. The pilots' women, children and babies saw what was happening. Reality set in, and then came the crying and screaming, the shouts of disbelief. They were abandoned. They were left on the beach in the Philippines, watching the big General, his family, his staff and their belongings cruise to the ship in the whaleboats, leaving them alone, unprotected and behind. I try not to ever imagine that scene. I try, but it haunts me vividly as if I were there watching, like some kind of macabre reporter watching a massacre. The ship, smokestack ablaze to make speed, disappeared too quickly over the horizon and from the sight of the hysterical women, children and babies.

They hoped against hope they would be rescued. Maybe the big General would send another ship. Within a week, other ships did arrive. Not ours, but the Japanese came frighteningly into view. Their attack boats were launched and they landed on the beach. Yelling and smiling, they trapped and butchered the screaming women, children and babies. The sons of bitches threw babies up in the air and caught them on the points of their bayonets. Some of the women managed to run into the forests, clutching their children and babies. They tried to hide in the dense tropical cover, but the forest couldn't hide them. The laughing Japanese used dogs to track and capture them, then raped, abused and butchered the forest women, children and babies.

4

I kept flying. I was sure that my wife and babies were safe. I thought they were on the ship with the big General. How was I to know that they were betrayed and abandoned? How was I to know that they were dead? How was I to know that the big General lied?

The Pacific Theater of the war heated up. I flew more and more missions from our new Allied base to bring back the wounded. I went further behind the lines to find the stragglers, and to scout for POW camps in China. This was dangerous flying. The Japanese didn't want us there, didn't want us to know about their POW camps. I encountered considerable enemy fire. Uncle's barnstorming flying techniques helped me bring back a goodly number of our boys. It was only a matter of time, though, before my luck was up and my plane was shot down. I tempted fate, flying further and further into enemy territory, rolled the dice one more time, and one more time, and eventually I lost. My plane and crew were shot down over China. The Japanese had identified, and somehow knew, my plane. They surrounded my crew and me as we crawled out of the wreck. In some odd, warped way, they respected me. I represented some kind of warrior, samurai maybe, to them. They respected me as a fellow warrior, but hated me as the enemy, the American. I was now their POW, and their prize, their special prize. My crew was not so lucky. They were beheaded in front of me. The Japanese used a long sword. That death was quick and merciful for my crew. I suppose it was out of some honor or respect for me to behead my men. I was as strong as I could force myself to be during the execution. No emotion. No motion. The Japanese paraded around the camp with their trophy heads on the bayonets of their guns. I never asked why they beheaded my crew and not me, and I never found out. Two guards marched me from the execution ground and shoved me into a large bamboo cage filled full with thirty or forty dirty and bearded men. Shredded uniforms fluttered with their every motion. Their nails were claw-like, yellow and black. As my eyes adjusted to the dim light, I saw their hair moving. Their long, matted hair was filled with lice, fleas and crawling parasitic things. They stared at me with the frightened, glazed, and fixed stares of tethered animals waiting to be sacrificed. Some opened their mouths to try to breathe. Sickness and stench permeated the close air. Most every one of them had rotten, broken and missing teeth, or stubs of teeth covered by black gums. Open sores oozed smelly puss and worms. Dirt, darkness and disease mixed with despair inside that bamboo cage. No hope. No escape. The living dead waiting for something, probably death. Now I was one of them.

Days, weeks, months passed. I saw many things as I, too, grew dirty. My long hair filled with lice, fleas and crawling parasitic things. I tried at the beginning to pull them off of and out of me, but they returned in even greater numbers to infest my hair, skin and bodily openings. My nails grew until they broke or split. I watched the smiling guards weed out the most frightened, the most disturbed, the most susceptible to screaming and the most intimidated from the bamboo cages. Weed them out to torture and experiment on them. Was it a plan, or were the camp guards simply cruel and bored? They shot the pleading POWs in various parts of their bodies. Some in the buttocks. Some in the arms. Some in the legs. Some in the gut. The Japanese doctors wrote things in a notebook.

One medical man in a white coat watched with a stopwatch. Timed how long it took our boys to lose consciousness. Timed the screams. Timed how long it took to die. Used the POWs for their experiments. Wrote it all down. Illegal, of course. Against the "rules of war," as if war really had rules. In the winter, the smiling guards selected more screaming subjects. Hosed them down with water. Timed how long it took them to freeze to death. Sometimes they'd combine the torture. Hose them down, and shoot them. The medical man observed and wrote it all down. Nazis must have taught them about record keeping. They wrote everything down. The POWs screamed, writhed, and couldn't escape. Death couldn't come quickly enough for them. They were not afraid to die. They were not afraid of going to hell. Hell was here. Hell was now. Death was Heaven, and heaven was welcomed.

I wondered when my turn would come. It never did. I was special, a prize. I would be made to watch. Unknown to me, I would never die by their hands in this way. My punishment was different. I was to watch, and suffer in the watching. For me, that was all that was different. No special treatment. No decent food. Same amount of dirt. Same raggedy clothes. Same fleas, lice and parasites. One thin blanket. One wooden bowl. In these things, we were all equal. My punishment was to watch.

I had to escape. I knew if I stayed too long, I would be too weak and too complacent to do it. Careful, though, I had to be careful. The camp was fenced with barbed wire. One gun tower. Smiling Japanese. That wasn't the only thing, though. I had to be careful who heard me. POWs got more rations for information. POWs who supplied information did not become "subjects" for the camp doctors. Information was the camp currency. Information meant survival and more food. Information meant no pain. That's simply the way it was. I had to be careful, and I was.

New POWs arrived regularly. I sized them up. Which ones

would be strong enough... physically and mentally... to keep a secret, to plan the break, and strong enough to die to let another guy get out? Hard to tell. Very hard to tell. I didn't want to play my hand. I simply didn't know... and too much was riding on it to choose badly. Then, an interesting thing happened. It was interesting to me, anyway.

The camp had a small Buddhist shrine. Funny when I think about it. A POW camp where smiling guards tortured, experimented on and killed our boys... funny, thinking of them as having a religious shrine. It was hard to put the two concepts together, but the camp did. Apparently Buddha had traveled in this part of China, slept here or washed here or something. Anyway, it was some kind of holy spot for Buddhists.

A strange visitor came into the camp one day. An American! An American in a yellow Buddhist monk robe! The guards let him in. It was surreal... they let him in! Apparently, he was a regular visitor, and had clearance to worship at the shrine. His gaze washed over us. He was intent on the shrine, and unconcerned with POWs. Man's cruelty to man was detached from him. The shrine, Buddha and his personal journey to perfection were his reality. He never spoke, not even to the Japanese. He arrived. The gate opened. He entered. He worshipped. He left. Sometimes the guards, who were Buddhists, too, gave him food. He bowed, never spoke, and left with the meal offering. Once, when he bowed, he was near our prisoner compound. He fascinated me. A white American with a shaved head in saffron robes moving around and through the prison stronghold, unmolested and unchallenged. I leaned on the bamboo bars, draped my filthy hands over the cross bar and stared at him fully. He swept the stockade with an all-consuming glance. He did this regularly. He never made eye contact with any of us filthy prisoners, only skimmed the full scene and left. This time, though, he stopped his visual sweep and focused briefly on my hand. He acknowledged in the shortest instance possible my Masonic ring. He then looked quickly at my eyes and then away and back to his Japanese hosts. He flung the robe covering his hands over his shoulder exposing his hands in their prayerful pose, and he bowed in gratitude to the guards. He made the point to me that he wanted to make. I saw his Masonic ring. We were brothers, brothers far from home. I was trying to survive in the enemy's camp, and he was trying to worship there. We were Masons and brothers. This bond was too strong to ignore. It was stronger than religion. It was stronger that politics. It was stronger than the war. It remained unsaid, but I knew somehow, some way, that he would help me escape.

The American Buddhist monk turned away from the prisoners' bamboo cages, and walked to the fortified gate. There, a sentry was manning his machine gun from his tower above the gate. The monk stood in front of the tower, bowed to the sentry and waited. The sentry received a hand signal from the commandant, bowed to the monk and opened the gate for him to leave the compound. The guards stood on either side of the opening gate with their rifles at the ready should any feeble but desperate prisoners make a break for freedom. None did. The monk walked barefoot through the open gate and disappeared as the gates were closed and locked behind him. I bit my lip, but did not smile. I wanted no one to know that somehow there was hope.

Weeks and months passed. The monk's visits became more frequent. Apparently it was some holy season and the shrine not only had the monk, but a contingent of oriental worshipers from the nearby country side. The guards and the commandant didn't care for this confusion inside the compound, but orders from higher up ordered them to let the faithful in. After all, they were praying for the Emperor, a god and their leader, to prevail in this war. The Commandant did as he was told, but balanced this order with tighter control of the prisoners. Worshippers milled about the common grounds. Prayer wheels and prayer flags littered the otherwise orderly and carefully arranged compound. We prisoners remained in lock-down.

The prayerful visitors, and the American monk in particular, strayed closer and closer to our bamboo cages. Prayer flags from the faithful adorned our cage's bars. The prayer flag streamers fluttering above the dust almost made this dung heap festive. The guards were vigilant, but allowed the activity. No guard tore away the prayer flags or prayer wheels from the faithful, or restricted their activities or locations. The American monk moved closer to our cage. He handed prayer flags and wheels to prisoners. He draped long stripes of prayer flags through the rough bamboo bars. The red, orange and yellow streamers of silk waved and sparkled merrily after he passed. The guards grew tired of watching the religious activity and began talking to each other. The rifles drooped downward as they joked with one another. The monk came to our cage. He handed each of the prisoners a prayer flag or wheel, and made a religious gesture as he did so. He pressed a flag in my hand and curled my fingers around it. He looked directly into my eyes before he quickly moved on to the rest of the prisoners, giving them prayer wheels. I squeezed my silk flag. I compacted it so that no part of it protruded from my fist. I dared not read it, for I knew it contained a message. I dared not read it until I was assured I was alone and unobserved.

Evening came. The worshippers departed for the day. The guards let us out for latrine detail and exercise. I went to the edge of the compound to relieve myself. With my back toward the tower, I slowly opened my prayer flag message. It hailed me as a Brother Mason. More messages would follow in this same manner. "Be strong and hope." I knew what he meant. He would help me escape.

The holy time lasted a period of weeks. The prayer flags became more focused in their messages. Each one added a vital detail, but taken separately, they would mean nothing to the guards. Diversions would occur. Weapons and supplies would be hidden inside and outside the prison compound. The worshippers while Buddhist and traditionally non-violent, were Korean and Chinese. Each hated the Japanese for familial and national atrocities, for abuse and injustices visited on them over the course of not only years, but also centuries. They vowed to be supportive of the American monk and us, even to the point of death. I closed my eyes in disbelief. I tried not to cry, but a tear came just the same. My job now was to gather trustworthy prisoners for the break. Out of the prison population of over 400, I could trust my life to only 29. The rest were too weak, too addled or too hungry. Hungry men talk for extra portions of food. I couldn't trust our break to them. I couldn't trust the weak, the addled or the hungry, none of them.

The plan to make the break was set for the last day of the religious holy days. Fireworks would be set off that evening and provide cover for our actions. Praying and meditating worshippers placed explosives at the base of each guard tower as they swayed and prayed. The compound was covered with strings of prayer flags and whirling with prayer wheels. The guards were counting on this day to end the religious interference. The impatient guards and sentries even tolerated being decorated with strings of prayer flags around their necks. Anything to end this camp disruption. The camp began to look more like a cruise ship, with the guards on holiday wearing Hawaiian leis. The festivities became more animated and loud as the evening hours approached. Later, I learned that the worshippers added more inventive and boisterous religious energies to the festivities to confuse and fatigue the camp guards.

Twilight came. The fireworks started with shouts from the worshippers. More dancing and twirling. They danced closer to my bamboo cage. More worshippers danced near the guard towers. They all raised their arms on a signal from the American monk. Weapons came out from under the robes and shot the locks off the bamboo cages and set off explosives at the bases of the guard towers. My men and I scrambled out and raced for the entrance gate as the towers crumbled beside it, leaving a nice hole for us to crawl through. We made for the mounds of earth outside the camp, mounds conveniently marked with prayer wheels and filled with grenades, bullets, small arms weapons, knives and rations. We dug our bounty from the mounds. It was what we had prayed for and hoped for. The commandant and his men were confused and began shouting contradictory commands to each other. They pulled the prayer flags from around their necks, and tripped on them as they ran for their weapons store. The fireworks continued in the sky and added to the confusion of the weapons' retorts on the ground. Our escape was undetected for about twenty minutes. Worshippers shot Japanese, and the Japanese shot them. Hungry prisoners pointed to the hole by the gate and yelled, "That way! Escape!" I later learned that some of the addled prisoners came out of their mental fog long enough to strangle the traitors. We heard the screaming, the fireworks, the explosions, and the shooting. Then we heard the vehicles. They roared through the hole in the compound walls and in our general direction. The land was fairly flat, dry and hard so they could drive all over. Some drove in circles. A few crashed into the sides and fronts of each other in their confusion, and in their haste and fury. Darkness helped us some, but the damn Japanese still managed to capture, wound or kill twenty-five of us. It was completely dark now, new moon, and the guards figured they had us all. They took a few spins around, yelling and honking horns, signaling to each other. A few of the vehicles almost drove over and crushed us, the four remaining free prisoners. We had dug ourselves into the ground in four of the handy mounds, invisible at night.

The guards sped back to the compound through the hole and around the fires that still consumed the towers and the bodies of the gate tower guards. The living worshippers and the monk had fled, had almost de-materialized in the confusion. Dead worshippers were left on the ground, and wounded worshippers were dragged to safety, to a prearranged spot by the living worshippers. The guards would worry about them another time. The camp grew silent, except for the tortured screams of the wounded and dying prisoners. They would die a horrid death. Loyal and brave, though, they never gave us away, never gave us away, right to the very end.

We knew the Japanese would eventually take a head count, figure who was dead, who was still in camp, who was captured and who was missing. Then they would come after us. With the fires and the explosions, and the torture ahead of them, the search party wouldn't happen until morning.

We dug out of our mounds. As we did, we saw and felt the tire tracks embossed on the earth beside our would-be graves. I remembered from my flight plans and maps generally where we were. I used the stars to roughly plot our escape to the Allied lines. It would be a long trek, and we began.

I was grateful that once we left the mounds the ground was hard. That made it difficult to track us. The Japanese would find the mounds, but that was alright. We moved swiftly, as swiftly as emaciated men full of parasites could move. We were driven. Two days of traveling, switch backing, hiding and eating off the land to save our rations. It took its toll. Two of the men started staring at the sun and calling to Jesus, Mary and Joseph. They said they had been safe at the compound, and wanted to turn back. We couldn't stop them. They had a spastic, crazed look in their eyes, and one boy's delusions fed off on the other. Ragged, filthy and demented from the trek, they grew louder and louder in their determination to return to the prisoner camp. We couldn't stop them. There is no convincing the insane into sanity. They turned their backs to us and stumbled toward wherever they thought the camp was.

Midday and warm, my buddy and I sought shelter from the sun and the vision of the pursuing guards. We heard the two demented begin to sing. They faded somewhat, but we did hear them as they grew weaker, collapsed to the ground, and began to carry on as if their decision were some type of celebratory act. They pulled out their remaining rations and tried to consume them all. More singing and retching. Can't force food down a gullet not used to it. It grew quiet. We slept and tried not to dream of the two "Prodigal Prisoners" returning home to the seething reaction of the camp guards.

We woke at twilight and the cool, darkening of the night. We moved on. The next morning as we made our stop in some scrub trees, we saw large carrion birds circling far behind us. Our two, confused demented boys? Maybe dead? Maybe almost dead? Maybe they somehow changed their minds and were trying to make their way to us, following us. Should we try to turn back? Could we save them? Maybe the Japanese found them. Maybe the Japanese hacked them up, and were thinking there might be more prisoners to grab, hack and torture. We decided our buddies were dead, one way or another. Can't go back. Must go forward. The vultures would clean up the landscape either way. Nature's food chain, nature's clean-up committee.

My buddy and I continued in the direction I charted. Five days, six days, twelve days. It began to rain as we descended from the foothills. The thunder was inspirational music to us. The lightening was power from on high. The heavy, falling rain caressed and soothed our scraped, broken and aching bodies. We lifted our filthy heads to catch the liquid torrents in our parched mouths. We welcomed the rain for its healing attempts, but the thickening mud slowed us, and made our movements more tedious as our feet were sucked down in the slippery muck. On the fifteenth day, when the rain stopped, we came over a small rise and saw camp lights on the coast. We heard the hum of aircraft taking off and landing. We could make out the white star and blue bars on the planes' fuselages. We were in friendly territory. We crawled the last miles until we could hear voices, voices speaking English. We stood up, waved our arms and hollered, "Americans! We are Americans! Americans!" With our beards, stringy hair, filth and ragged clothes, we looked like two Rip Van Winkles, emerging from the twenty-year sleep. We yelled again and again in our pitiful and croaking voices. G.I.s in presentable, and recognizable American uniforms came running up the rise. Their equipment and weapons clanked on their belts, legs and thighs. "American, we're Americans. Joe Di Maggio! Babe Ruth! Wrigley Field!" we declared, then sank down in front of them in the mud, and lost consciousness.

I woke up many days later in a hospital bed, washed, shaved, trimmed and connected to a number of IVs and a feeding tube. A good-looking nurse was taking my pulse. When she saw my eyes open she said, "Welcome back. I'll get your doctor." The doctor came running when he knew I was conscious. "You've had quite an experience! You are one tough SOB," he exclaimed. "Welcome back."

I learned my buddy was not so lucky. He had one set of powerful worms and parasites that perforated his bowels. Peritonitis filled his abdomen and took him off to Jesus. He never woke up from the time we collapsed on the hill. I was it. I alone survived. Of the twenty-nine, only me. Only me.

As I began to speak again, I told my doctor and nurse that I knew where the POW camp was in China. I told them about the torture and the experiments. I told them I could fly planes, and I could take a plane to the camp and rescue our boys. There was no time to lose. I was ready. I wanted to go now. I sat up to emphasize my point, my voice rising, my arms connected to needles waving and fingers pointing. My spirit was ready. My body wasn't. I fainted. I wouldn't fly today.

The next time I woke up, I was surrounded by a group of high-ranking officers. Their brass was blinding to a man coming out of an unconscious darkness into the overhead light of intensive care. I blinked my eyes in disbelief. Officers? Brass? I must be dreaming, or hallucinating. They had been told I wanted to fly, and where and why I wanted to fly. They told me they understood that I knew how to approach and land outside the prison compound, and they wanted me to do that, but not today, but one day when the flight surgeon certified me to fly. I must rest now. That made sense. The flight surgeon and all. It was rules after all. OK. I asked about my wife and babies. They said they were not the ones to talk to me about my family. They would have the Chaplain come in to talk to me. They excused themselves and said we would talk later when I was stronger. I was puzzled and weak. I agreed. They congratulated me for making it out of the camp. Said there was a mighty fine field promotion in it for me, especially as I was willing to fly back into that hellhole to save our boys. They'd be back in a few days when I was stronger to arrange it all. I thanked them and fell back into a drugged sleep.

The Chaplain visited me the next morning. I learned the terrible truth from him. My wife and babies weren't alive. They were dead. He didn't need to spell it out for me. They hadn't been evacuated from the island. They were abandoned. We were lied to. They, the women and children, were lied to. They were left to be slaughtered. They all were dead. The Chaplain talked to me of God's mysterious ways, and that my family was now with Jesus. I told him to fuck off. I told him that the damn General had lied, that there was no God after all, and to get the hell out of here with his namby-pamby fairy stories about God and Jesus! He raised his eyebrows, opened his mouth, stepped back, speechless and left the room. He had come there to offer some comfort in a Methodist sort of way. I wasn't buying. The General lied. Damn General! He killed them. They died. They all died. I never saw that Chaplain again. From that day on, I resolved to grow stronger, heavier, to fly again, to bomb the hell out of the Japanese, and to never again believe in God.

Food, hygiene and exercise. I became a driven machine; no longer was I a mere man. I lived for two purposes only, vengeance and destruction. The medical staff and the flight surgeon were amazed at my swift recovery, my weight gain and my daily determination to fly back into the camp.

Six weeks later I led my first squad of planes behind enemy lines. We spotted the camp, bombed and buzzed it to disable it before we landed to retrieve our boys. I touched down first on the hard, flat clay, and I was prepared. Grenades, knives, small arms, belts of ammo. I strapped it all on and leapt from my plane. Fires and explosions marked the destruction of the camp. Our boys were screaming from their bamboo cages. I ran straight to them and shot the locks off, pulled the doors open and yelled, "You're free. You're going home, Americans!" They yelled "Hoo-ray!" and "Thank God!" as they walked out into the sunshine, holding each other up, staggering and trying to take in the enormity of what had just happened to them so quickly. Surely, they thought, they must be dreaming.

A few of them cowardly, damned Japanese were still hiding, the ones who weren't dead. I wanted them. I wanted to slaughter them the way they had slaughtered my wife and my babies. I found them! One by one. I sliced one's throat. He gurgled in his blood. It would take him awhile to die. One pretended to be dead. I pulled the pin from a grenade, put the spitting and gurgling Jap on top of him and shoved the grenade under them both. The explosion lifted them both into the air and sprayed body parts across the parade grounds. I decapitated some of those butchers. I grabbed some of the squealing pigs by the hair, kicked them and cut off their body parts and stuck them in their mouths before I gouged their eyes out and slit their throats. I shot a goodly number in the gut. A shot in the gut hurts more, and takes longer to kill a man. I smiled as they grabbed their wound, writhed and screamed. At the end, I was not tired, not in the least. I was angry that I had run out of enemies to kill. I searched for more. Finding none, I satiated myself with cutting off fingers, ears and noses from the dead and tossing them on the ground like some much litter. I went into the base headquarters. I wanted all the records I could find... didn't have too much time; the fires were getting close. I stuffed a bunch of the notebooks I had seen the camp doctors write in and ran out of the flaming shack.

We searched the camp to assure that all prisoners were found, and that all of the Japanese were dead. We hauled down the hated flag, threw it on a fire, and hoisted the American colors. All our boys and flyers saluted and cheered.

The sun shown through the haze of smoke as we flew out. We entered safe air space and our destination, the Allied air strip and base, was only a few hours away. That base would be the closest thing to home that these boys had seen for months, and in some cases, years. The boys settled down as we flew home.

The base was in sight. I broadcast over the radio and P.A. system that we would touch down in fifteen minutes. I contacted the tower at announce our arrival, and heard cheers from the boys in the tower. We circled the base and wagged our wings so everybody would know that we were on our way in. The boys were wide-awake and staring out the windows. When they saw Old Glory waving and floating in front of the glowing sunset, they sent up a cheer! Someone started singing "America the Beautiful," and then the "Star Spangled Banner." There were no real singers in the group, but it was Magnificent! Even I was surprised by the water that welled up in my eyes. We touched down on the long runway. It was deserted at the end, but as we drew closer and closer to the hangers and the base buildings, more and more boys and girls were populating the runway edges. Even at that speed, I could see that they were cheering and waving and crying... girls and boys. Some were whistling with two fingers in their mouths. Jeeps were parked there with their drivers blowing the horns and flashin' their headlights. We got to the hanger and it was a mob scene. Medical personnel out front, doctors, nurses, orderlies, corpsmen, gurneys, IV poles, Big Brass off to the side, mechanics, armed G.I.s in fatigues, chaplains, cooks, radiomen, traffic tower guys running down from their posts, firemen, ambulances, even a dog or two twirling around and barking. I stopped the plane and cut off the engines. Once the propellers stopped, we slid the doors open and we heard the full brunt of the welcoming shouts, whistles and cheers. It was deafening! The medical personnel surged forward to retrieve the boys. The stronger of the boys inside the plane helped lift the weaker ones down to the personnel and the gurneys. Some of the boys jumped out of the plane, dropped to their knees and kissed the dirt... American dirt. They were home! I sat in my seat, and rested my head on the wheel. We did it. We really did it.

When all the boys were accounted for and taken by the personnel into triage for evaluation, I checked all the controls for exit, rose from my seat and made my way to the open door. I jumped down, deep in thought and filled with happiness, my boots landed on the hard packed dirt. I looked at those boots thinking how muddy and splattered with blood, Japanese blood, they were. When I looked up, the cheers and shouts and whistling started again... waves of cheers and shouts. They called my name and yelled, "Hero... Hero... Virgil... Hero!!" I stopped, overwhelmed. I started forward again with my head down. Hands reached out to touch me and slap me on the back. "Hero... Hero!!" I'll never forget that. Never.

As the days passed, our reconnaissance planes spotted more POW camps in China. My crew and I volunteered for every flight. We had to get our boys out of there. The crew had seen what those damn guards could and did do, and so did I. We never hesitated. When a new camp was spotted and we got the coordinates, we were ready. Our missions were dangerous as we carried little ammo... we saved our space for the boys, but we went. Once in a while we could count on some fighter cover, but most of the time we went in alone. Alone and low. Surprise, don't you know?

When we left the base and ran onto the tarmac to scramble and fly, the base went on alert. As many as could, lined up to pat us on the back, tell us they'd see us soon... hopin' they would, anyway... and cheerin' us on.

This was our mission. Fly in low, surprise the damn camp guards, blow and burn 'em up, land, rush in to finish 'em off... the bloodier the better... chop 'em up... get our boys out of their holes and cages and onto the plane. I continued to search for papers and documents... stuffed them in a duffle bag. One more circuit around the camp. Anything

Japanese and movin' was stabbed and chopped. With all our boys out, we torched what remained of the place... purified it, so to speak... and took off for the Allied base. I radioed out ahead our ETA and the conditions of the boys so the medics, nurses and doctors would be ready. Sometimes we lost one or two of the boys on board... they were so bad off... but they died smilin'... they were with Americans, and they were goin' home.

The war was windin' down as most wars do, and my crew had fewer and fewer camps to clear out. Mostly, the yella' Japanese were either runnin' away or killin' themselves, hari kari, don't you know, save face and family honor and all that. Hard to imagine... torture and slowly kill captured American boys, and then worry about "savin' face." Hard to fathom, but that was their damn code. Our missions became less and less dangerous, and fewer of my crew were injured. More routine-like, fly in search and rescue.

One day I was summoned to the CO's office. I went in, saluted and stood at attention. He asked me to sit down. This was strange, I thought. He told me to make myself available the next day around noon at the main hanger, and to wear my dress uniform. I wanted to ask "why," but you don't really ask "why" of the CO. He talked about what a good crew I had and how many boys we had saved and how many families were goin' to be beholden to my crew for what we did and all that. He even poured me a double shot of his fine Tennessee sippin' whiskey. He raised his glass to toast my crew and me. I joined him in that toast. We clinked glasses and oh, my, that whiskey slid down just fine. He talked some more, small talk, really about nothing. We finished our drinks, he shook my hand, I saluted. He saluted, and I left.

The following day I was ready and dressed early that morning. The base was fairly quiet. Only one or two planes landed. None took off. That seemed strange to me, but this day and the CO's orders to me seemed strange too. A few minutes before noon, I left my room and walked to the main hanger. No one was in the halls, and as I glanced into the hospital/recovery rooms, the beds were empty. Stranger and stranger. The big doors to the main hanger were unlocked, but closed. I swept my hand over the side of my hair and wrinkled my brow. This was curious. Opening the big doors, I saw every medic, every nurse, every doctor, every patient, every officer, every pilot, every crewman, every "anybody." They were waiting for me and once they saw me a groundswell of cheers and "HOORAHs" and applause overwhelmed me. I stopped dead still. It kept up. I opened my eyes and took in the gathering. The cheering kept up. I saw a platform set up at the other end of the hanger. The CO was there. Flags were set up behind him. Civilians in suits were sprinkled in amongst the big brass. Even from this distance I could see the gold gleaming on the big brass's covers. Music, patriotic music, started playing from some place up front.

Two Marines in full dress uniforms, complete with swords stepped from either side of the doorway. A "Permission to escort you to the stage, Sir?" They both gave me a salute. "Permission granted." I returned the salute. One went ahead of me and one went behind me. The mass of people parted like the Red Sea. When we arrived at the stage, the Marines each stood beside the stairway facing me. They saluted me again. "An honor, Sir." I returned the salute and climbed the stairway to the stage. The music, the applause and the cheers continued. Hands and arms were swaying in the air. Patients who shouldn't have were standing next to their IV poles, holdin' on with one hand and slappin' the other hand on top of it. The brass and the civilians and the CO on the stage were applauding as well. It was for me. It was for me. I glanced around the stage. One of the cheering civilians was my Ohio Senator. I recognized him from his round size and the vest he always wore to try to disguise his round size. He saluted me and smiled a broad smile. A chant started up, "Virgil, Virgil!!!" The drums beat time to the chant. It did go on. The CO held up both hands to eventually calm the throng and the drums. The chant and the drums sputtered out, and the mass of people sat down, as did the honored guests on the stage. I was escorted to my chair by the CO and asked to be seated. The Marines had climbed the stairway during the celebration and positioned themselves at attention on either side of the stairway facing the audience. The flags fluttered slightly in the breeze created from the exuberant applause and display.

In a quiet moment, the CO called up the Chaplain for an invocation. I wasn't keen on it, but there you go. It was short and to the point and my name was mentioned many times asking for God's blessings on me forever, and thanking me for saving so many boys, and surely my reward in Heaven would be nearer to the Throne, etc. , etc. I bowed my head and waited for him to come to the end. He finally did. The CO then went on to introduce the line of guests... admirals, generals, my Senator and others. I can't remember them all. Too much. Too much. He then called up my Ohio Senator to the podium. My Senator walked in front of me, stopped to face me, stuck out his hand to shake mine and slapped me on the back. I shook his hand. He slapped my back again and proceeded to the speaker's podium. Oh, Lord, I thought. That man can talk. How long will we be here? Mercifully, he was to the point and not long-winded. He mentioned me many times, and each time a swell of cheers rose up from the crowd, and that slowed down the show. Of course, each time they gave out their cheers and whistles and applause, I smiled and tried to wave them down, but they would have none of it and kept it up. Even stopped the Senator.

Finally though, the Senator got through his remarks about my captivity and escape, my personal losses to the war, and my leading the rescue planes in to bring back our boys. That set them off again... especially the boys on gurneys and IV poles. They gave all their strength to yell and whistle and clap. At last it settled down. Two generals were called up to the podium. I was called to the podium. The crowd started up again. I held up my arms to help quiet them. They did. The Senator had a long leather box on the podium. He opened it, and asked the two generals to help him do the honors. He asked me to move closer. I did. "From a grateful nation to this hero, who gave of himself without regard to his personal safety, did save from horrible captivity over 700 Prisoners of War... we now bestow upon you our highest Honor... " or words to that effect. The three of them lifted out the medal and its thick ribbon. I saw it. My God! The Congressional Medal of Honor. The Congressional Medal of Honor! It must be a mistake... . they all took a bit of the thick ribbon and lifted it over my head. The Senator adjusted the Medal so that it was centered on my chest. He and the Generals stepped back and faced me. They saluted me, as did the Generals behind me and the Admirals. I saluted the three, turned to salute the rest of the brass and saluted the crowd of boys and medics and nurses. A roar went up again... whistles, pounding the floor with crutches, clapping, cheers, yelling my name like a cheer, "Vir-gil, Vir-gil, Vir-gil!!!"

After that, the brass all came by me on the platform to shake my hand. The roar kept up. I was overcome... a wonder I didn't faint dead away. The CO came from the back, shook the two Generals' hands and the Senator's hand. Everybody was smiling and happy. The Senator and the brass all sat down. The CO kept me at the podium... had his arm around my shoulder... asked me if I had anything I wanted to say. What could I say after all that? Well, it went something like this, "I am an American. I am proud to be an American. I did my duty as I saw it. I love my country and I will fight every enemy who tries to hurt my country, our country... and I love every one of you.." I raised my arm to gesture over the crowd and the roar started again. Someone told me later that it lasted for a full five minutes, even the brass clapped that long. I finally settled them, and the CO came back. We were finished with the ceremony and we were all to retire to a reception. Real food, steaks and cakes, and those who were medically certified, would have two beers each. A roar went up again. This time I don't know if it was for me, the steaks or the beer... or some combination of them all. The platform guests and I exited first. Many, many hands slapped my back as I passed by. More hands shook my left and right hands. I was a hero. I was their hero. Boys rose up from gurneys to touch me. "God bless you, Virgil!" came from the lips of the religious. The rest chanted my name and yelled "Hoo-Rah!" The smoking light was lit, the steaks were tender and everyone who was medically certified, and could, enjoyed his two beers. I'll never forget that outpouring of genuine love and admiration... never. I fingered the medal to make sure it was real. It was. This was all real. I would never forget it. Never.

The war eventually ended as all wars do. I had the G.I. Bill. I could have gone back to medical school to finish that one more year, and become a doctor. Many people asked me later why I didn't. It was hard to explain, but I couldn't. I had killed too many men, too many... what kind of a doctor would I have been? I was a killer... a legal killer, of course, but a killer, nevertheless. I was no kind of man to be a doctor. Besides I drank, drank a lot and swore. Couldn't much sleep at night... nightmares, you know. I saw my wife and babies... imagined them being hacked up by the damn Japanese... damn, smiling Japanese stomping through the forest with their killer dogs lookin' for the defenseless women and children. It was too real to me... only drink would fatigue me and tame my anger. I wanted to kill again, but I couldn't. No one to legally kill. The war was over, and now the Japanese were our "friends." Think about it, the Japanese were now our "friends."

I did have my periods of sanity, though. Sometimes I was even pleasant. I met a nice woman whose husband was killed in the war. We understood each other, and we got married. Stayed married for over twenty years. Both of us confessed that we would rather have been with our first spouses, but that wasn't the way the cards were dealt. I took a job at the shipyard, and she kept house. It was a type of normalcy. She helped me through my nightmares. We went to the VFW Hall for gatherings, and one day followed another. Never had another child. Neither of us wanted any... been through too much, too much heartbreak, too much sadness, too much loss. We did have a white Persian cat, though... but no dogs. Dogs were in my dreams, and she didn't much like them anyway. As the years went by, she came sick, and was down with heart disease. A massive heart attack took her away one day, as the ambulance carried her off. The cat died shortly thereafter... out of grief and heartbreak, I expect.

Alone. There I was, alone again. I kept the place just like she left it when she went away... her glasses still on the coffee table... the letter she had been reading there too... the shawl she wore, draped over a chair... a silly framed photograph of our white cat yawning, lookin' like it was talking. I realized how much I missed her... and in my own way, loved her. Eventually, all her things... this shrine to her... was covered with greasy dust and cobwebs. It didn't bother me. It was my sanity, this shrine to her. For a moment... a split second... I could fool myself that she would be comin' into the room any time, and that the cat was just down the hall, and would be following her. Never happened, of course. She never came back into the room. The cat never came back from down the hall. Just me here with all the greasy dust, cobwebs and memories.

With her gone, the nightmares became more vivid, and I drank even more. They say drink is a depressant. Guess it is, but it took the edge off. After a while, I lost track of time, maybe a year, maybe five years. I couldn't trust myself to drive. My car stayed in the front yard, the tires went flat and the thing rusted up. I paid some neighbors to go out for me... bring me stuff... stuff to drink, something to smoke, and some snacks to eat. Some of the folks said I shouldn't drink so much. They were probably right. Some of them tried to give me religion. I swore at them. NO religion... there is NO god. God wouldn't let what happened to my wife and babies happen! NO religion. NO god! They didn't come back. I couldn't be converted, and I guess that rocked 'em.

I eventually found a neighbor who liked to drink too, could drive, and needed a little spendin' cash. He and I shared a few, and he never talked about god or religion. I liked that guy just fine.

One day I'll die. One day I'll be released. One day I won't have to dream. I won't need to drink. I'll be free. I'll be released from this, this horrible, parasitic, and all consuming pit of anger and loss. Death, I welcome it. Pleasant, quiet, soothing, dark death. My final release, my final freedom.

Virgil stopped, sat up straight, took a sip from his ever present small, dirty glass of whiskey, took a drag from his stub of a cigarette, turned and asked his visitor, "Well, girlie? You came here to help me from some agency. I don't know if there is anything in this whole, wide world that you can do for me... 'cept maybe fill this glass for me." He held it out toward her.

The Social Worker who had been sent to assess and help him, and who had listened to Virgil, was silent. What, indeed, could she do for him?

VIRGINIA

This story was relayed to the Social Worker in just this way. I can't say if it's true or made up, but it was reported to her in just this way.

Virginia died an hour ago in her home, in her bed. She knew death was near. She wanted to be at home when it came. She was, and this made her last days happy. Ormand, her husband, knew she was dying. Intellectually, he accepted it. Emotionally, he was angry, distraught, and rudder-less. Virginia was his whole life. Without her, he was a shell waiting for his turn to die. Ormand was fifteen years older than Virginia, and he was supposed to die first, not Virginia. This wasn't the way it was supposed to be. His love, his life was gone. He was quiet. He was very quiet, alone with Virginia in the room in which she had chosen to die. He looked at her, sweetly remembering her vitality, their ballroom dancing, their four grown children, their three granddaughters, her giving nature, her religious loyalty to her Catholic faith, her beauty, and acknowledging the empty feeling that was beginning to fester in his heart, and the knowledge that the emptiness would only continue to grow and grow, until it consumed him with his own death. He looked at her hand clutching her rosary. Even in death, she held tight to it. He rose and kissed her forehead, a forehead that was becoming cooler and colder. "It should have been me," he thought, "it should have been me." A loud knock on the main door at the front of the house broke his reverie. "What?! Who?!" he thought. The knocks came again. "Oh, front door," he concluded. He stood, reluctant to leave Virginia, gazed at her once more, turned and walked to greet the persistent knocks.

Solemnly, he made his way down the narrow hall, passing the other bedrooms, passing the kitchen, through the living room to the front door. He opened it to find three lady neighbors.

"We've come to see Virginia. How is she today?" They didn't know. "Please come in, ladies," Ormond stated simply. They did, and he closed the door. They each started chattering about why it took them so long to come by and they hoped they weren't intruding but they simply had to see Virginia. Ormand did not immediately answer. His quiet pause puzzled them. Ormand was usually so polite and forgiving. "Virginia died just a little while ago. I've been with her. Would you like to pay your respects?" Their eyes opened wide. They hadn't expected this. People don't die at home. People die in hospitals. They looked at one another. They paused. Of course they would like to pay their respects. Of course.

Ormond sighed slightly. He hadn't expected visitors, especially now, but here they were. He led the way slowly down the narrow hall to the main bedroom. The lady neighbors looked around, scrutinizing the housekeeping details of Virginia, seemingly having forgotten that Ormand just told them that she was dead. They pointed into the kitchen to each other at the dishes piled in the sink, the smell of garbage and grease, the darkened small room dirty and disorderly. They tittered as they passed the small bedrooms used by unmarried sons, clothes piled on clothes, on beds and chairs, all in the unlit rooms in seeming shades of charcoal and gray. Rolling their eyes to each other they acknowledged to each other, "No real housewife lives here." And further implying, "My home would never look like this." They passed by the small bathroom, its rumpled towels wadded over towel bars, a ring of thick blackish scum visible even at a quick glance, circumscribing the bathtub about ten inches from the bottom, and the lid of the toilet as well as the seat proudly at attention, leaning against the toilet tank with its faded, unidentifiable colored chenille seat cover slipping off the lid. They pointed, raised their eyebrows and continued to follow Ormand. They would have much to discuss later in their own pristine homes. Ormand noticed nothing. He was focused on once again being with Virginia. He reached the bedroom doorway. There she was. His beauty, his sleeping beauty.

She looked angelic in her white gown, her white sheet drawn up to her bosom, her graying dark hair softly resting on her neck and shoulder, her hands, still pink, resting on the sheet, her right hand grasping the rosary. Unlike some corpses, her eyes closed naturally. She looked more in repose than deceased. The lady neighbors stopped in unison. A small, bedside lamp was the lone illumination, not only in the room, but in the entire house. This small lamp cast a strangely velvet-like glow on Virginia's features. They were not prepared to view death like this, not in a bedroom, not in a private home. A hospital, yes, a viewing room in the funeral home, yes, but not here, not at home. Ormand heard none of their tittering and suspected none of their criticisms. His eyes only saw his Virginia. He turned and spoke, "Isn't she beautiful?" They paused, and in harmony said, "Oh, yes, Ormand, just beautiful. Like a princess." They glanced around the room. Messy, messy. They stepped cautiously toward the deceased, examining the housekeeping, as well as the departed. Sheets haven't been ironed. Each slightly shook her head in disbelief. Dust was on the bedside table. Dust was on the headboard and footboard of the bed. The throw rugs needed a good washing, perhaps even needed to be thrown out. The blanket and coverlet had seen better days and they too could have benefited from some bleach and ironing. Ormand sensed none of their thoughts. They had come to pay their respects to his beloved. That was enough. Ormand continued to gaze at Virginia. Maybe if he wished and prayed hard enough, she would cough and awake from her sleep to be with him again. She looked so perfect, so peaceful, so far away from her pain, so happy. Maybe. Maybe. Ormand sat in the chair he had placed by her head; he leaned on her pillow, closed his eyes, prayed and wished. Maybe. Maybe.

The three inspectors saw Ormand beside Virginia with his eyes closed. This was their opportunity to squint their eyes and more thoroughly examine the details of the room. They turned their backs on Virginia and Ormand as one, and absorbed the housekeeping deficiencies as they saw them. Framed pictures of the Virgin Mary and the Sacred Heart of Jesus were on the wall facing them and gazing down at Virginia behind them. Brittle palm crosses were stuffed into the frames from many years of Palm Sundays. Dust covered the picture glass, and spider webs and long strands of dust connected the frames with the ceiling. The three glanced back at Ormand. His hand was on Virginia's. His eyes were still closed. They smiled slightly and returned to peruse the dresser. A dust-filled lace runner was topped with loose coins strewn across it. On the edge were dusty, dog eared holy cards in a bunch; strings attached to labels of clothing were tossed on top of the cards; dried carnations in an almost dry glass-ribbed, bud vase were positioned between the two framed pictures; a half eaten chocolate cookie and an open pack of peanut-butter cheese crackers completed the litter on the lace runner.

Three bottom lips tightly frowned into three top lips in disgust. Dirty, dirty. They glanced back; Ormand's eyes were still tightly closed. They thought he might have fallen asleep. His head shifted and his cheek lay flat on the pillow with Virginia. The crowns of their two heads touched. Both were in repose. She dead, and he living, though not wanting to be. Emboldened, they dared to touch the dresser. Sticky and dusty. They looked at each other. The tales of Virginia's housekeeping were true. Messy and filthy. They dared to open a drawer. Shaking their heads, disorganized garments oozed out. As they began poking and pulling at the drawer's contents, they noticed their shadows on the wall becoming more and more defined. A light behind them was becoming brighter and brighter. Even on their backs, it became bright and brilliant. They squinted, and dared to turn around. They thought Ormand had awakened, caught them digging and turned up the lights behind them to expose their meddling.

Ashamed and exposed, they turned around. The light grew more intense. They raised their arms to shield their eyes. Ormand blinked awake, shut his eyes quickly, stood and stepped back from Virginia's bed. They all looked at the light in short glimpses. Two areas of the brilliant light began to sway and shimmer slightly. The four, terrified, but mesmerized, were frozen by the sight unfolding before them. The shimmering continued and two forms, even brighter, began to take shape within the light. The shapes looked like two men in gowns, and the shapes of men positioned themselves on either side of Virginia, their faces focused on her. They raised their hands slightly over her and spoke softly only to each other. They did not acknowledge any of the other four inhabitants in the room. Their intent was only on Virginia. The glow from their light illuminated and radiated Virginia. She began to shimmer in the strength of the light. The glowing men raised their hands high in unison and gazed at the ceiling, not so much the ceiling itself, but beyond, far beyond the ceiling, beyond the roof, beyond the trees, beyond the sky, beyond the sun, moon, stars and galaxies. The four were paralyzed and remained transfixed. Their eyes could not adjust, but they could peek out from under their arms for brief glimpses of the men.

"What! Oh, my God!" The three lady neighbors finally exclaimed, "What is happening?" They hugged each other in fear. "What is this?"

Ormand glanced at Virginia. She was shimmering and radiant. Her eyes remained closed, but she was smiling. Ormand was comforted. He smiled. The women began gasping and squealing, hugging each other more tightly for protection. They began to become hysterical, each feeding off of the other's fright. The brilliant men placed their hands on Virginia, and slowly turned their gaze to the three women. "Have no fear," they said in a low and ethereal voice, "we will not harm you. We are here for Virginia."

"What? Who are you?" they became bold. "What would you want with her?"

"Virginia is chosen. We are Raphael and Gabriel. We are here for Virginia."

"Those are angels," one of the three whispered to the others, "Why do angels want Virginia?"

The men turned back to Virginia, "When I was hungry, you fed me. When I was thirsty, you gave me drink. When you did this to the least of my brethren, you have done this to Me. Virginia, your work on earth is done."

One of the women sniffed and snidely remarked, she thought unheard by men, "Look at this place. She did nothing."

Raphael glowed more intensely, turned and looked directly as the speaker. His eyes were white-hot orbs. She froze. "Virginia's work was not in this house. Virginia's work was in the world. She read the Word; she became the Word through her work. You had an angel amongst you, and you saw her naught." The room pulsated with light and rumbled with tremors.

The women thought they heard thunder outside. They were certain, when asked later, that multiple flashes of lightening criss-crossed the sky as Raphael spoke to them. They could stand the light, the trembling, the thunder, the lightening and his words no longer. They bolted for the door. Running down the hall, they began to scream for help, "Help, Police! Help us!" They punched the door open, ran to their closest home, scrambled in, locked the door and peeked through the recently dry-cleaned draperies.

Virginia and Ormand's house began to glow in its entirety, windows, roof, walls, and shrubs. The women couldn't bear to peek through the draperies. They lay screaming on the recently steam-cleaned carpet. Their husbands would later find them hysterical and unable to prepare a decent dinner that evening.

Ormand heard Raphael's words as well. They comforted him. He was in awe of the events and of the angels, but he felt strangely at ease in the presence of Gabriel and Raphael.

He watched as they placed their hands on Virginia. Raphael, being in tune with human suffering, turned to Ormand. "Be at peace. We have come to carry the soul of this good person, this angel, this saint to Heaven. All is well. You will see her again in Glory. You have had this saint for a little while on earth. We will have her for eternity in Heaven."

The house shook. A great rumbling as in an earthquake was heard and felt. The glow was blinding. Raphael and Gabriel bore the sacred soul to Heaven in a blaze of light bright as a comet's trail. Then the house and the surroundings quieted and its rooms grew dim again. Only the single lamp illuminating the bedroom provided a soft velvety light. Virginia's earthly remains lay lifeless on the bed. Ormand stood beside them and stroked her hair.

ROSA

Rosa was about seventy-five, an old seventy-five, when I met her. She was a medium height, very thin black woman with eyes that seemed to always be in the "surprise" mode. She wore only dresses, mainly housedresses, with an apron over the skirt. I never really saw her hair. It was always tucked up under a variety of scarves she tied into a turban shape. Her feet hurt her, so she wore very wide, flat shoes with soft men's sox. She also suffered from arthritis in her knees, shoulders, neck, hips and hands. Her finger and thumb joints were swollen most of the time from this ailment. Consequently, she moved carefully and slowly in her little, dim and kerosene scented apartment. The television was usually tuned into an evangelist or otherwise religious show. If none was available, Rosa switched on the radio to a religious talk show or gospel hour.

Her home in this apartment was in a seedier part of the large city. Drug dealers, prostitutes and otherwise unscrupulous characters rented the apartments surrounding her. She kept her windows locked and nailed shut. Her door had a number of locks, deadbolt and chains, to protect her from a wrongful home invasion by her neighbors' business partners. There were other old people sentenced to housing in these apartments. Rosa did not really know any of them. No one sat outside. No one went to another apartment to visit. No one left the security of his apartment to become a target for stray bullets or abuse. Only quick trips from the apartment to a waiting car, driven by a relative or church member, were dared by these old people. Rosa's activity pattern was the same as theirs. Rosa's family was either dead or seldom mentioned. The center of her life was her church and the weekly ceremonies it held. Sunday's services could last until three o'clock in the afternoon. Rosa told me how she "testified" and became "filled with the spirit." When she was "filled with the spirit," she danced a dream-like agitated dance, a dance of which she had no recollection, a dance in which her church members told her she leaped from pew to pew shouting "Hallelujah!" and "Amen!" She didn't know how she did it. She had no pain, no slowness and no memory during the dance. Only when she returned to her apartment did the aches, fatigue, and stabbing pain return. There, in her apartment, after she locked all her door locks and took off her church shoes and the large church hat that matched her church dress, did she collapse on the dark sofa in the dim light and carefully place her swollen feet on the littered coffee table.

Rosa had been married long ago. She called her husband, "Dick," and for some unknown reason, he called her "Dick" as well. In those younger days, "Dick" and "Dick" were much healthier and wilder. Hard liquor was a mainstay, and violence was the preferred way to handle marital discord. Rosa told me of the stabbings she had visited upon "Dick" each time she learned of his marital and drunken infidelities. She confessed that she too was unfaithful when under the influence of the liquor. "Dick" would find out, beat her and sometimes stab her as well. They each bore the marks of battle and punishment. Rosa told me these scars were common amongst her set of friends. There was no such thing as marital counseling then, only fists, knives and sometimes, guns. I never did know what happened to Rosa's "Dick" except to say that Rosa did not kill him. He just faded away from the rest of her stories. Perhaps he ran off, or perhaps he died an old man. I never knew.

Rosa had a number of grandchildren of whom she was

proud but never saw. I don't know if they lived somewhere else, another state or city, but they never came to her dark apartment. She had some framed photos of children on her living room wall. She waved at them in a broad gesture and called them her babies. She never directly answered my questions as to whether these photos were her grandchildren, or her "play" babies, that is, babies she cared for and loved, but not her blood kin. Rosa never mentioned her child or children. I didn't know if she had one child or more than one child. She was very close with this information. Anyway, no child or children came to visit her.

Rosa's only visitors were her Pastor, a trustee and the driver of the church van that carried her to the weekly services. Rosa said the Pastor had supernatural powers and that he could see into her soul. He told her she had a black soul covered with the sins of her youth. He told her that only he could help her cleanse her blackened sinful soul. She had to obey him. He knew her every thought and he knew if she were truly obedient, even when she was out of his sight. If she didn't obey him, and she died in the state of un-redemption, she would be cast into the deepest part of hell to writhe and torment forever in the fiery flames. His penetrating look into and through her eyes made her tremble and shake. She knew she had been a wild and bad young woman. She had broken a number of the commandments many times. She had begged to be forgiven every Sunday. She "testified" and was filled with the Holy Spirit and danced a sacred, if un-remembered dance, but Pastor said her soul was still black and tarred with layers and layers of sin. She had best obey him, otherwise she would be forever in the fiery flames. She tithed from her little income. She tithed at each and every service and ceremony she attended each week. Sometimes it was one ceremony. Sometimes it was three ceremonies. After a number of months, Pastor said he could see parts of the layers of tar and sin beginning, just beginning, to slip off of her soul. Pastor said he even saw a pin hole of bright light starting to shine through the corrupt tar layers of sin. Rosa smiled when he told her this good news. The tithing was taking effect. Perhaps she would not be cast into the fiery flames forever. Perhaps there was hope if only she lived long enough, and obeyed the Pastor.

The Pastor then shared a secret with Rosa. Perhaps she could hurry the procedure along, and slough off those tarry layers more quickly by doing something else, by thinking about others, by sacrificing for them. Believing her time on earth was limited, she felt it was important to move this process along. Rosa asked the Pastor, "How?" The Pastor said he would bring the Trustee to their next visit. He was true to his word and the Church Trustee came with him the following week.

The Pastor asked Rosa if she loved her grandchildren, if she wanted to see them protected and if she wanted them to have the finer things in life that she never had. Her answer was as he expected. "Yes, yes, yes!" she shouted. "Good," he said, "the Trustee will show you how to do this." The Trustee was a confidant of the Pastor and one of his twelve, chosen evangelists. This man of the church, brought here by the Pastor, would help Rosa cleanse her soul and assure her of a life in heaven when the time came. What a blessing she thought.

When the Pastor and the Trustee left, Rosa had purchased life insurance policies for each of her grandchildren. The premiums would be automatically withdrawn from her account each month. She would not have to be bothered with writing a check or money order. It would be so easy, and her grandchildren would be covered. Rosa, the Grandmother, had done a good thing for these children, and the Pastor looked into her eyes and said he could see the black layers of sin falling away from her soul like shingles from a roof in a hurricane. In no time her soul would be bright, clean and perfect, like his and the Trustee's. A real blessing, a real blessing, Rosa thought. I won't go to the torment of the fiery flames. I won't. I won't!

Months passed and Rosa's little bank account was depleted. The bank said there was no way to stop the automatic withdrawals. She had signed for them to continue in perpetuity. Rosa said the Lord would provide. A number of charities stepped in to pay her utilities and buy her food. She was found eligible for state medical aid so her doctor's bills and her medicine were free. She was able to pay her subsidized rent for her apartment in the war zone. Rosa didn't mind. Her soul was being cleansed and the Pastor said she was becoming almost anointed and holy. Rosa was elated.

Rosa felt she was indeed becoming anointed and holy. She told me about a thick, long black snake that somehow slithered into her house, and coiled itself under her armchair. Its head darted out from time to time, and in the gloomy dimness, Rosa saw it. Its head was the size of an orange, and it was shiny and black as Lucifer. It rested momentarily, and then began a slow extension into her living room. It came toward Rosa, methodically and purposefully. Rosa was unafraid. She knew she was close to being anointed and holy. She knew her soul was almost cleansed and pure. She moved along side of it slowly, and unlocked and opened her front door that led into the common hallway. She then opened the common door that led into the parking lot. In the past she never would have left these two doors open and unattended. Her criminal and "no 'count" young neighbors watched from the hoods of their expensive, new and shiny cars. "Yo, Rosa!" They called when they saw her. "Want to come out and have some fun wi' us?" they laughed and jived, poking each other in the arms and the ribs with their elbows. Rosa ignored them, and went back into the living room where the thick, black snake was maneuvering across the greasy carpet into her efficiency kitchen.

Armed with a broom handle, Rosa faced the snake and raised the broom handle, "Out, out you devil snake!" She shouted, "In the name of the Holy God and His Son, Jesus, I command you to get out!" The snake coiled up and faced Rosa. It swayed and opened its wide mouth as if to strike her. "I command you in the Name of all that is Holy to get out! Get out, Devil! Get out!" The parking lot gang heard the commotion and joked that Rosa had really gone off. The snake looked at Rosa and closed its mouth. It lowered its head, uncoiled its body, turned around and slid out the two doors. The snake was eight feet long. It greeted the parking lot gang outside. They screamed and jumped on top of their carefully waxed and polished cars. The snake reared its head to get a closer look at them, lowered its head and glided its way into the woods behind the apartments. Rosa saw it go as she stood in the common hallway. She slammed the common front door and her apartment's front door. God was good. He had saved her from the Devil snake. She must truly be anointed and holy now. The parking lot gang was still screaming outside. There were gunshots, but they missed the snake and only shot their cars. Rosa sat down on her armchair and put her swollen feet on the cluttered coffee table. Now she knew, and so stated, that she would not go to the fiery flames of eternal torment. She was holy and anointed and would surely go to Heaven.

The charities continued to help Rosa. The state continued to provide her medical care. Rosa died a few years later, and no criminal types ever bothered her in the golden days of her declining years.

NAOMI

Back in the late '90s (1890s), everyone in New York loved Coney Island, especially my brother Herbert, and me. Coney Island was the summer escape from the city heat for rich and poor alike... sure, the rich had their cottages in Newport and Maine, but the rich liked to "slum around" Coney Island from time to time, takin' in the noise, hot dogs, carnival rides and the boardwalk on the beach, and the rest of New Yorkers came to Coney Island to cool off, wade in the surf and have that new, cold treat called ice cream. Dances were held on the boardwalk in the evenings, amateur talent contests were held, and theatricals were presented in front of feverish audiences fanning themselves in the shade. As the sun set, a sea breeze blew on shore from the green ocean to wash over, cool and re-civilize the heated city folk. Evenings on the beach and the boardwalk were somewhat boisterous, but mostly the noise was harmless play and banter.

My mother and father owned and ran a small but stately hotel on the island. Their rooms were filled with fresh flowers. Only fresh vegetables, and fresh fruits, served on white, spotless linens, by staff in black and white were good enough for Mother and Father's guests. Our hotel's broad, shaded veranda was stocked with cool, white rocking chairs and gliders that overlooked the pounding, blue-green sea. Sea birds floated on the sea foam breezes and currents. All was intended to induce conversation, laughter and relaxation. Inside the cool, louvered, and darkened rooms the fragrance of lavender linens, mingled with salt air to sooth the sleepers and readers relaxing within. It was very, very pleasant and our hotel was always full. We did well, and lived quite comfortably.

Herbert and I attended private school. I had my own horse and English tack. Our world was ideal and perfect. Herbert went on to college, and at 15, I began my ambitious plans for a "coming out" at 17. Then our world changed.

Father suffered a mighty heart attack and died. No warning... no symptoms... just sudden death. A good man taken too soon. Mother became stiff and mechanical, walking through her days, but not really living. As was the custom, we went into mourning for a year. Mother and I wore black, and Herbert wore a black armband at college. We still had means, but Mother knew she could not run our hotel alone. Still grieving, she hired a smooth talking manager. He pretended to care for her, and for Herbert and me, too. Even as young people, though, Herbert and I saw through him. He was a manipulator and a cad. Mother didn't see it, and over the course of that mourning year, they came to an understanding and became engaged. At the end of Mother's mourning period, plus two months, they married. I believe Mother simply felt she had to. Mother never said she loved him... not the way she had said it over and over about, and to, Father. She liked the manager well enough, she needed a man to run the hotel with her, it wasn't proper for him to be there alone with her, so, they married. Women back then didn't run things by themselves. She needed a man. And he was it.

Herbert was in his third year of college. My "coming out" plans were postponed. Mother, Herbert and I decided it would be best; Mother had been through a lot and needed some time to let things settle out. Besides, I was only 16, and my entry into society could wait until after I had ended my education at Briarhaven Girls Boarding School. Beaux began coming around. I went to dances... actually, I was quite good at dancing, too... belle of the ball, you might say. Some things went along as normal, but it really wasn't the same, nor would it ever be after Father's passing.

The stepfather ran the hotel, and enjoyed the company of the maids. I would hear them giggling when he made complimentary remarks in his deep, soothing voice about their figures or complexions. As time went by, he singled out one maid who was most responsive to him. One day I followed them very carefully, and saw them disappear into a room at the end of the upstairs hall. Herbert heard about it from me when he came home from school. The stepfather's actions upset Herbert unbelievably, and he confronted the stepfather who yelled that Herbert was a liar! Mother heard their confrontation, and separated the two. "Quiet, quiet!!" she protested. She didn't want to hear anymore such talk. "Hush! The guests would hear." She placed herself between them, put her hands on their chests and separated them. They glared at each other, turned from each other and walked away. We never knew if Mother believed Herbert... she never said. She did move into a separate bedroom, though, and replaced the hand-tinted photograph of Father on her dressing table, as it had been during their marriage. From that day on, Mother drew more and more into herself. The stepfather carried on as if nothing had happened. He escorted the maid to town for supplies, and stayed longer than usual. Mother's eyes were moist and red when we caught her unawares. The hotel continued to be full and successful, but Mother's spirit and joy was gone.

By and by, Mother became ill... a cancer, the doctor said. She could have an operation that might help. Mother refused. "Why?" she said, "why bother?" Herbert and I pleaded with her. She refused. The stepfather said that was her decision, and went on as if the cancer killing his wife had no bearing on him. He made all the proper remarks to the guests and the public regarding her escalating illness... how he was so concerned... how he had tried to do everything he could to keep his precious wife with him... how he loved Herbert and me as if we were his own children... and how he was bearing up and going to run the hotel just the way she wanted it to be run... and thank you, kindly for your concern for me. They believed him. Herbert and I did not.

The disease became painful as the cancer consumed her. Morphine and laudanum eased some of the pain, but clouded her mind. She stayed in bed, gazing at Father's photograph in her infrequent, clear moments. The stepfather busied himself with the routine of running the hotel. He then began curious visits to Mother during her conscious moments... he carried papers into her to sign... told her they were invoices and bills. She signed without questions and slipped back into her drug induced, pain-free, semi-consciousness. Herbert and I tried to stay with her at all times, but the stepfather watched for the opportune times when we both were away for a few moments. Mother made some remarks to us about signing papers, but she was so addled as to time and place, that we took no mind to her statements... we should have, but we did not. We told her we loved her and that we wanted her to rest and to get better. We said all the things you say to the one you love... all the things you say when you know there is nothing else to say to the one you love that is dying, and you both know it.

Mother died. She was buried beside Father in our New York City family plot. Mother and Father. Together. Herbert and I went into mourning once more. After the service and burial, Herbert and I returned to the hotel and our rooms.   The next day the stepfather called us into the hotel office with Mother's lawyer. We assumed we would learn of the terms of Mother's will and our share of the hotel, etc. Herbert wanted to finish college. I wanted to finish my education and "come out." This was not to be. The lawyer said he was very sorry, but Herbert and I had no inheritance or claim to the hotel. Mother had signed over the hotel to the stepfather only, and all her assets to him as well. He alone inherited her money and property. It would be at his discretion if he were to grant us any access to or consideration from Mother's estate. The lawyer asked the stepfather what he planned to offer us as the children of his deceased wife. The answer was short and revealed his true self, "Nothing. You have one week to collect your belongings and leave the hotel. If you don't, I'll have you arrested for trespassing!" The lawyer was astonished, and his wide-open eyes showed it as he leaned back away from the stepfather in disbelief. There was nothing, though, that the lawyer could do. The stepfather had had Mother sign over all her rights and ownerships to him. He'd even had a new will drawn up giving him exclusive and singular rights as her only heir. Two maids witnessed it. Mother never knew what she was signing, but it didn't matter. According to the lawyer, it was legal. The stepfather smiled.

Herbert and I collected our belongings, Father's photograph and remembrances from amongst Mother's things. The stepfather watched to see each thing we took... nothing valuable... he had plans for them. Herbert, with the education he had, and the friends he had made in college, secured a job at a big New York department store as a buyer. I lived with him in a small apartment in the city. After a month or so, I decided I needed to find a job to help bring in money. With only Herbert's wages, there was no money for me to finish my education. I was too young for marriage; besides, the beaux stopped coming around when word got out that Herbert and I were penniless. What could I do? What was I even good at? I could ride a horse reasonably well. I could create a menu for dinner and oversee its preparation. I was a good conversationalist... but those aren't really moneymaking skills. I had to face the fact that I was being prepared to marry and run a home, not make a living. End of story. For a few days I was depressed. I took a walk downtown and watched a sign go up, "Dancers Wanted for New Productions." I could dance, and what did I have to lose? I auditioned the next day, and I was hired. The girls who got in were the first of the famous "Rockettes," me included. Herbert wasn't too sure about this life on stage... was it proper? But what could he do? I had made up my mind and that was that. I was a good little dancer, able to make those high synchronized kicks and even learned the tap routines. I had strawberry blonde hair... natural, too... and my bright blue eyes. I was a stunner, if I might say so myself... and so proud of my big job in show business... for about six months anyway. I'd told them I was 18 and able to work. Well, they checked and found out I was almost 17, but not 18. It was illegal to hire me, so I had to go... and go I did. Herbert said not to worry. I would stay with him, and when I was 18, he'd find a job for me at the department store. I found comfort in Herbert's love for me, but I still wanted to help the two of us in some small way. I made the meals, kept the apartment clean, saw to our clothes, visited Mother and Father in the cemetery, and watched neighbors' children for a small fee. I didn't have to be 18 for that, and that small fee was a help.

The year passed, and Herbert was true to his word. I was hired as a clerk in the men's haberdashery department. I selected shirts, ties, handkerchiefs, suspenders and silk stockings that coordinated with the suits the men bought from the male clerks and tailors across the hall. It was easy and pleasant work for me... putting a costume together for a fashionable and classy client. This, I could do.

I began to develop a special relationship with many of my female customers... wives of important men who wanted their husbands to stand out, fashion-wise. I seemed to have a good sense of what went with what, and the customers appreciated it. The wives would ask for me, and together, we made their men gorgeous! I met many of the suppliers and vendors. I'd ask for certain colors and patterns with certain customers in mind, and since I always sold them; there was no problem with special orders or holding back unique items for my customers.

One of the salesmen came around my counter more than would have been expected. He was a good-looking man, made a decent living being a regional supervisor, and on the move, up and down the east coast, tending to his accounts. He asked if he could take me to dinner. He said he had asked Herbert's permission, and I was pleased that he had. We began "courting" and then became engaged. We married, and I traveled with him sometimes. He seemed to want me to stay at home in our little house on Long Island, and he didn't want me to work anymore at the department store. No wife of his would work... how would that make him look? I fussed around our home. Had Herbert to dinner from time to time, but I was bored. I thought I'd surprise my husband. I knew his itinerary, and had the train schedule. I hopped on the train bound for Richmond... wouldn't he be surprised to see me! I arrived in Richmond and went straight to the hotel's front desk. I asked for my husband's room number, and received a curious look from the clerk. He said, "Mr. and Mrs... " I stopped him, "But I am Mrs... " He corrected me and let me look at the register... plain as anything, "Mr. and Mrs." I thought and straightened myself. "Give me a room and charge it to my husband. I'll stay as long as he does." I went to my room to freshen myself, came downstairs and positioned myself in the lobby so I could see guests coming in, but they really could not see me. About 6 p.m., they came in, arm and arm, laughing, strolling up to the desk and asked for their room key. They turned to mount the stairs, and he saw me and went white and red. Stood absolutely still. "Naomi... how?... when?... why?" His mind and body moved in slow motion. The woman on his arm sized up the situation, pulled back her arm and stepped back. "Who is she?" she said, knowing, but not knowing. "My wife, Naomi." he stated, dropping his head. She said she needed some money to get back to Atlanta, and that she'd get her things from the room. She held her hand out for the cash. He fumbled in his pocket, brought out some bills and pushed them her way, staring at me the whole time. She left, and I went to my room. I ate alone. When he checked out, I checked out. I followed him down and up the east coast, staying in my separate room, and watching young women rush to him in each city as he arrived, so glad to see him... until they saw me. Then they backed off and avoided him like a poison. I sure spoiled his fun. He had to pay double bills, one for him and one for me. When it was over and we were in New York once more, I had Herbert help me find a lawyer and I ridded myself of my first husband. The settlement was quite generous. The grounds in New York were only adultery, and as for evidence, I had plenty. The judge rebuked him and ordered the house sold, with proceeds coming to me, and half of his salary to come to me until such time as I should remarry.

Oh, the pain on his face... the pain on his face. I'd found him out, and I had triumphed.

Herbert helped me resettle in the city. I returned to the department store, but not in the haberdashery department. I didn't want to see him ever again. I was placed in house wares and furniture... somehow, I got into interior design. And, I was good at it. I studied the movie sets and magazines. I went to the library and studied historic settings. I followed the up and coming designers... the all white rooms, country English, art deco... you name it, I studied it. I was able to "read" my clients. I guess I was a really a good sales woman. Eventually, the store wanted to expand down South. They wanted me to go down South and set up their furniture, home furnishings department, so I did. I hated leaving Herbert, but the trains still ran and I had plenty of money. I would see him regularly and frequently.

Southern people, for the most part, only wanted one style... plantation style. Antiques, oriental rugs, Chinese porcelain... I loved it. This style reminded me of home and happier times with Mother and Father. I used the authentic brighter colors, not the pastels so common then. I developed quite a following... one rich lady sent me to another and so on... I even went across the state... in their limousine with their chauffeur, of course. You might say I enjoyed the "high life." I lived through the Depression, and really never knew there was a Depression. I bought antiques and grand pianos and oriental rugs and artifacts from razed mansions. I enjoyed beautiful things, and I had them.

I was not without male companionship, but I did not marry until one very handsome policeman ticketed my car for going too fast. He was gorgeous. I tried to plead my case out of the window, but he'd have none of it. Straight as an arrow. He didn't even ask for my telephone number. I asked for his. Happily, he wasn't married, never had been. I was lucky. We dated. He was uncomfortable with my making more money than he did. I said it didn't matter. That only made it more for "us." When we got down to serious talk about marriage, I told him of my ex-husband and the settlement. That was not important to him. He was earning a good living and was up for promotion. We went back and forth. He was not one to "live in sin" just for money. I didn't care, but I didn't want to lose him. We married, and I cut back on my hours at the store. I had all the beautiful things I had ever wanted, and now I would have him! Herbert came down from New York to give him the "once-over" and his blessing. Herbert approved and gave me away. Life was good. I, for some reason was not able to have children, and Herbert never married, so I never had any nieces or nephews. We did like dogs, though, and we had small ones and big ones, hairy ones and smooth ones. Some I even taught to sing with me while I played the piano... that glorious grand piano with the butter-yellow, leather piano bench. I would play, the dogs would sing, and I would look out the large windows at the boats passing by on the river. I loved my husband, and he loved me. He was an excellent police professional... I say that because he was far more than a policeman. He helped the children who had no father, and those whose father was of no use. I think he was a saint, he said "No." when I called him one, but to me he was a saint, anyway. We had many friends, and invited them to our home all the time. As years went by, my husband reached a certain age, and he had to retire from the force. He didn't want to leave his work, but those were the rules. He knew the rules, he obeyed the rules, but it began to depress him, being away from his work and his colleagues.

They came by the house, and he joined the group of retired policemen. He involved himself in community events, but it wasn't the same, and his spirit began to fail. His health declined, and I became his "cheerleader" and nurse. At the end, he never left home for two years. The friends stopped coming to visit. The dogs and I sang to cheer him, he did smile a little, but it wasn't enough.

One day, he simply turned his head to the wall beside his bed, and stopped breathing. He willed and released himself from a place and circumstance that were not to his liking or in his control. His was a large funeral with Safety Officers of all kinds standing at attention, with black bands on their badges. Even the K-9 officers and their dogs were there. The K-9 dogs' badges also had small black bands on them to commemorate the loss of one of their own. A long cortege of vehicles stopped traffic for almost one mile in respect to my husband. I wore black, with a heavy black veil over my large black hat. Herbert came from New York to escort me through the ceremony and burial and reception. I returned home that night with Herbert, exhausted and grieving. The dogs greeted me, wagging their tails, yipping and smiling as only a dog can smile. I hugged them and told them that "Daddy" was in heaven and wouldn't be coming home anymore. When I said these words to my furry babies, I finally cried. I had been very brave all that day, but I wasn't anymore. The dogs rallied around me and made little whimpering sounds... they seemed to understand. Herbert wanted me to come back to New York with him. I couldn't make that decision now, and in my heart of hearts, I really didn't want to go. My home was here. I was 77, and I did not want to start over in New York. Besides, I couldn't take all the dogs to New York. They weren't apartment pets, and looking at their faces, I just couldn't leave them... just couldn't... not my "babies."

So, alone with my dogs, I remained in our home. Herbert returned to the big city, promising to visit from time to time, but somehow managing to come back only once or twice. He was old, too. His health began to fail over the next year, and travel was out of the question. We kept in touch by telephone, usually by Herbert calling me and paying the long distance bill. Money was becoming short for me. I thought the police department would be sending me a pension check, well, they did... every month the check arrived for $15.00. Yes, fifteen dollars. That really was a surprise... $15.00. With my little Social Security and a $100.00 pension from the department store, I was able to eat and feed my dogs. Pretty soon, I began drawing out our savings to pay utilities and real estate taxes and repairs and automobile upkeep and once in awhile, a new hat for me and treats for the dogs. As I grew older, so did the dogs. They suffered with ailments just like we do... arthritis, diabetes, cancer and heart illness. Medicines and treatment for them was expensive, but I paid it and did without for myself. Herbert wanted to send me money. He had an inkling of my money situation, but I never really spelled it out to him. I didn't want to take from him. He was failing and needed his resources to pay for help for him. Three years after my husband died, so did Herbert. I borrowed money from friends to see him buried next to our parents. I guess I never thought Herbert would die and leave me. I'd never been without him, never been all on my own, it was so odd, so final... so very alone. I looked at the empty plot waiting for me next to Mother. There we would all be, the four of us, reunited one day... Herbert, Father, Mother and eventually, me. It was comforting in a way... to never be alone again.

I returned home. Even with my old, friendly disabled dogs, the house was cold, empty, and so quiet. The number of friends coming by dwindled. I had no money to go out with them... to go on trips... to go shopping... to go to lunch. They came by as a kindness, as a charity. I found that hard to bear. I began to make friends with my immediate neighbors... chatting about the weather, our ailments, our childhood, but nothing deep or confidential. That helped. The dogs, despite the wonders of veterinarian science, died one by one. I had them buried in a pet cemetery and I stood over their caskets dressed in my black clothes and hat and veil. I suppose some people would think I was a little "touched," dressed in mourning for a dog, but I was in mourning. Even later, when I thought of my good dogs, and their kindness of sharing themselves with me, I lapsed into mourning again. When they were all gone, I couldn't stay in the house anymore. It was too alone, and besides, I had run out of money. The savings were gone, and I had begun to sell pieces of furniture and oriental rugs and special pieces, like the small vestibule light that Herbert had salvaged from a Vanderbilt mansion being razed. So many memories. I hoped each piece would be happy... as if it were alive... in its new home. I moved into a little one bedroom, first floor apartment. My piano with its butter yellow leather bench went away. The Chinese Chippendale dining set and the Wedgwood service for twelve and sterling silver flat wear and tea service all went away. I had my memories... but no room for my old friends. I made do and smartened up my apartment with what I had left. Chinese patterned red draperies with bamboo roll-up shades behind them, plump stuffed chairs and couches, a small reproduction oriental rug, solid wood dining table and four chairs, oriental patterned sheets on my high bed, that needed a stool for me to ascend it for sleep, or a "lie-down" when I had a headache. I never took aspirin for my headaches. I tied a white strip of cloth, scented with lavender around my forehead and lay down. It worked every time. I simply had to be patient. One day, during a "lie-down," a miracle happened.

I had made friendly acquaintances from amongst my neighbors and had told them of my love for my departed dogs. How I wished I could have a dog, even a small dog, but I knew it was impossible. I set my mind to living in the apartment until... well, until I joined Herbert and my parents. But, one rainy day as I lay down with my headache band on, the doorbell rang. It rang sharp and determined, not soft and slow. It must be another salesman... but out in the rain? I pulled the curtain back to look at who would be out at my door in the rain. Not a salesman, but, my neighbor lady, her hair all stingy and wet with rain. I wondered why she didn't push that wet hair out of her eyes, and then I saw why. She was holding a furry bundle in her arms, "Naomi! Open up!" I did. She squished in... her shoes were soaked and they squeaked as she came into the living room out of the rain. "Look at this, just look at this!" I closed the door to the fog and windy rain. She put the bundle on the floor. "Look at him!" I did. He was a very dirty and a very wet little poodle, charcoal gray with large, round, black eyes. He looked up to me. He had a sort of pleading look on his face. "Get me some heavy sharp scissors, please, Naomi." I was puzzled, but I did as I was told. She held the small dog. At first I thought she was going to cut the dog, but I knew her to be a kind person... she wouldn't come into my home to cut up a small dog. I watched her carefully, nevertheless, and then I saw what she was doing. She was cutting a leather collar from the dog's neck. "Some bad person put this collar on this dog and his fur has grown over it... it's digging into his skin... and it has to come off." I held the little guy while she "operated." He whimpered and squirmed. She finally got it loose, and pulled it gently away. "Just as I thought! Some skin had grown to the collar. I'll be careful." Slowly, the wiggling little dog was extracted from the strangling collar. His neck was rubbed raw and bleeding in some places. "We'll have to clean him up. Do you have a big towel, peroxide and soap?" Of course I did. We took him into the bathroom, ran the tub full of sudsy hot water and scrubbed him down. At first he complained, but as the warm water soothed his dirty and raw body, he relished in the comfort. Pushing the suds aside, I could see the water turning black with streaks of bright red blood running through it. We rinsed him until the water ran clear and wrapped him in a thick towel sheet. He settled and was quiet. Somehow I never questioned that I would help this neighbor with this dog, and somehow she never questioned that I would. Once I was holding the dog in my lap in the towel on the couch, she told me the story of finding the dog running in circles on a busy street in the horrible rain, cars flying past him on both sides. "Someone threw him out of a car onto the street," she said. "I saw it. I stopped my car, ran out and captured him. We came directly here. I thought you might like him. He needs you and you need him... just look at his neck... poor thing. Look at him look up at you. I think he likes you. Well?" Well, what could I say? I named him "Baby."

Baby was my joy. I taught him to dance on his hind legs, and made little hats for him to wear while he danced. I almost think he enjoyed this dancing. But maybe it was my singing and clapping my hands, and giving him my complete attention that he enjoyed. Whatever it was, he was eager to perform whenever I brought out the little hats. What a sweet Baby. My neighbor was right. I needed him and he needed me. Baby's neck healed, but fur never grew in that ring of meanness around his sweet neck.

I was lucky enough to find people to help me. Some took advantage of me and my situation, but others were generous. One lady helped me out by running the vacuum and dusting. She, though, wanted to use my department store credit card. I let her as long as she paid it off every month. She did for a while, but then it backed up and the store was calling me. I had no money, so I stopped that arrangement. She went away after that. The city nurse who visited the old people visited me. She had some of her patients make soup and she delivered it to others. When I needed cash, she would buy dishes from me. I knew she didn't need them, she was a widow and just a little younger than me. I never knew what she did with the stuff, but it sure helped me out. Senior citizen case workers visited me and saw to it that I was hooked up with every benefit I was eligible to receive... fuel assistance, food baskets, health insurance from the state, food stamps... anything to stretch my little money. I had to take care of Baby, he came first. If I didn't have Baby, why should I live? Some of the families and couples who delivered food baskets seemed to really like me. They took me out to dinner and into their homes. They remembered the holidays and my birthday. When cash was short, they bought what remained of my antiques and trinkets. That stash of goods was shrinking, though. I didn't want to take outright cash... I wasn't that way... I wasn't a charity. Sometimes, I would make a special dinner for my visitors... a recognition... a "repay" if you will. Spaghetti with my homemade meatballs was a favorite with them.

Baby got older, and so did I. It is the nature of things. I began to dream of my mother and my father, of Herbert and my husband. I even dreamed of the horse I owned as a girl and loved... all gone... gone from a happier, younger and friendlier time. Some people believe that when you start dreaming about your lost loved ones that you are about to cross over to join them. That worried me, not so much the crossing over, I was ready for that, but what would become of my Baby? I had to make plans. The nurse said she would be honored to care for Baby. She thought he would be a good companion for her old Boston terrier, "Killer." I contacted the funeral director who saw to the arrangements for my husband. I wanted to be cremated, cheaper you know, and to be buried in my husband's grave. They allow that. One of my favorite case managers gave me a beautiful red, silk oriental tunic. I thanked her profusely. I said it was so beautiful that it will be the last thing I would wear. I would wear it when I was cremated. I could see she had a puzzled look on her face, but then she realized it was mine to have, and mine to use as I saw fit. For that, and the fact that it made me happy, she was happy.

I didn't need to worry about a home for Baby. He was fifteen, he had slowed down... the veterinarian checked him, completed tests, shook his head sadly. "It is cancer, Naomi. He hasn't long. There is no pain; it's that type of cancer. He will simply become more and more fatigued until he goes to sleep and doesn't wake up. I'm so sorry. I know how you love him... had him for almost ten years. I am sorry." I cried and took my Baby home. He rested on my lap during the day, and slept with me at night. I sang softly to him, and he seemed to smile. I know he liked it. He didn't dance anymore. He didn't care to eat... only a little piece of chicken. He only wanted me, and I only wanted him. By and by he did fall asleep... and my Baby did not wake up. I laid him out with his toys and little hats. I kept him with me for a full day... talking to him and stroking his curly hair... crying all the while. I knew what had to be done, but I didn't want to do it... so, it was done for me. The nurse came by on her regular visit. She saw me keeping vigil over my precious Baby. She hugged me, stroked Baby and said she would take care of it. She called the pet cemetery people to come get Baby, and ready him for a funeral in the pet cemetery. They came as the nurse and I were having some herb tea that she made. They were very gentle and carried Baby in a special container. They said a ceremony and burial would be held in two days. I heard the nurse talking to them softly at the door. I saw her take some money from her purse and give it to them. They left and the nurse called one of my neighbors to stay with me until the funeral. What sweet people there are on earth! My neighbor came with food and smiles. "No trouble, no trouble at all." Once she was established with me, the nurse left. I had headaches and bound my head. My neighbor said it was lack of food, and made a thick chicken broth. It was delicious, and I did feel better. In two days I readied myself for Baby's funeral. I wore my black mourning suit, hat and heavy veil. Some people wouldn't understand. Baby was just a dog, they'd say... but I loved him, and he deserved my respect. He was the last of my "line." Everyone else was gone. All gone. And I would be alone once more.

Baby was buried in style. I was able to stroke his fur one more time in the sunshine, before the lid was closed and he was lowered into his final resting place. They call it "closure." And that it was. Closure... final closure.

I never wanted another dog after Baby. I was ninety, and would soon be ninety-one. Not fair to a dog to give him to so old a lady as me. I'd play with my neighbor's little Pekea-poo... sweet dog, of course, but he was not Baby. One day for me was almost the same as the last, and would be the same as the next. I was weary and told the nurse and the caseworker as much... weary, weary, weary.

One day, about a year after Baby died, the case manager completed the story. Naomi went to sleep, and like Baby, never woke up. The arrangements had been made. The funeral director saw to her final dressing in the red, silk Chinese tunic. No viewing. No ceremony at the funeral home. The cremation reduced Naomi to a small box of remains, the size of one of her shoe boxes. She was transported in the dignity of the hearse to the cemetery. A new case manager's husband, who was a Lutheran minister, presided over the last words and prayers. The old case manager had brought a display of flowers... the only ones. It almost covered up the box of Naomi's cremated remains. The nurse and two neighbors completed the mourners at the grave. A few words... the Lord's Prayer... two readings from the Bible... and a blessing from the minister... and it was over. It seemed anti-climatic... ninety years on earth, all the experiences, all the life, and all reduced to this... so little, so little. It just didn't seem right... but there it was. The tiny group left the cemetery. The funeral director pulled back the sod from Naomi's husband's plot and interred her on top of his vault. The old case manager wondered if Naomi maybe would rather have been buried in New York beside her parents and brother, but Naomi made her arrangements, and it was done. Somehow, the old case manager thought, Naomi would find them all in the great beyond, no matter where she was finally buried. As she continued her walk to her car, the old case manager thought of what Naomi had said not so long ago, "I'm not afraid of dying... I'll be with all my good people, and you know what else?" The old case manager shook her head. "I saw Baby in my dreams for three nights in a row. He had on his little hat, and he was dancing... he was smiling and prancing for me. He seemed to be saying, "Where are you? What are you waiting for?" I woke up from those dreams singing to Baby like I used to sing to him when he danced. It was a happy dream." Naomi then turned, looked at the old case manager with a beaming smile, how bright and happy she was, as she said, "I will be so very, very glad to see him again in heaven. Yes, I will. Yes, I will."

The old case manager smiled as she continued her walk to her car. She smiled as she remembered Naomi's words and pictured her with her mother, her father, Herbert, her husband and her precious Baby... ... yes, Naomi was finally happy.

ISAIAH and VIVIAN

It was hard to tell if Isaiah and Vivian were married, or if they simply understood each other and lived together. It didn't really matter. Whatever it was, it worked for them. They shared a small, squarish, cinderblock house with a flat roof that they rented from a White man who gave it to them "cheap." The house was on a short, gravel, dead-end street with spindly trees bordering the dirt path leading from the street to their home. Tufts of grass tried to grow in what passed for a lawn, and thick, gnarled roots from dead and chopped-down trees punctuated the ragged yard. Two, large, clear, plastic bags filled with empty aluminum beer cans, each about four feet tall, stood at attention on either side of the grimy and battered front door. These bags belonged to Isaiah. He collected aluminum cans for extra cash and stored them in these bags. Two bags like these would bring in over twenty dollars, and he kept them close by for safekeeping. It wasn't that Isaiah was so neat, or that he hated litter. These were his cans. He had drunk the beer from these cans, and he would use the cash he collected when he turned them in to the recycler to buy more beer. It was a system, his system, and it worked for Isaiah.

The cinderblock house contained three rooms and reeked heavily of the kerosene used to heat the place. The front door opened directly into the center and main room, the living room. It contained their 13 inch, black and white television, two worn and tattered arm chairs, one straight backed chair between the arm chairs, two, sticky and dusty end tables, one beside each arm chair, and a coffee table covered with papers, junk mail, candy wrappers, miscellaneous scraps of food, and old paper cups or smudged aluminum cans. The space heater in the corner sparked and popped as it struggled to heat the entire house, however, heat stayed only in the living room. The fan on the heater worked intermittently, and didn't spread the heat to either one of the two adjoining rooms. It was 80 degrees in the living room, and 60 degrees or less in the other rooms. Vivian and Isaiah spent most of their time here. It had the TV, and the heat.

The front room of the house, closest to the road, off the living room, was a disorderly and unlighted bedroom. Looking through the gloom, I saw many black, plastic bags of used clothing given to them by the visiting nurse. They were piled on the bed, the floor, and up to, and almost covering the single, drafty, dirty window. Some of the clothing had been pulled out of the bags and strewn around as if to somehow sort and categorize it by types of clothing. The bedroom door was open, but the room was cold and stayed cold. Transparent curtains fluttered with the gusts of wind that came easily and often through the cracked panes and rotten trim. Peering into the bedroom, I guessed it was used only for storage and sorting, but not for sleeping. When I asked if the house had a bathroom, Isaiah motioned that it was somewhere off in a corner of this gray, dark bedroom. Cold there, too, I thought.

The back room of the house was a sort of kitchen. It, too, like the bedroom, was cold, dark, gloomy and dirty. Teetering cupboards were abandoning their moorings on the walls, and leaning into the room. Cupboard doors stayed open, pointing at the floor, and revealing Isaiah and Vivian's few plates, cups and bowls. Boxes and cans of food, some open, some sealed, were shoved and stuck between and on top of the dishes. A dirt floor, swept weekly, held a wobbly, wooden table and the table's two mismatched and cracked chairs. When it rained hard, water poured through the cracked kitchen walls and onto the dirt floor. Rivulets of mini rivers wiggled across the floor and collected at the lowest point under the table to form a sloppy, shiny mud hole. Sometimes the table tipped sideways when it rained too hard, and when the floor softened. Isaiah and Vivian didn't go into the kitchen at all when that happened. The overall atmosphere of the house was smelly, uninviting, and filthy. Vivian and Isaiah spent their days, and possibly nights in the living room. A charitable organization brought them "meals on wheels" five days each week. Because of this, meal preparation, and attendance in the "kitchen" was minimized. Besides, Isaiah filled up on beer, and I suspect Vivian did as well, but not to the extent that Isaiah did.

Throughout the day, Vivian and Isaiah sat side by side in their old armchairs watching the 13 inch black and white TV. Game shows were their favorite, and "loud" was their preferred TV volume, even when guests were visiting. Conversations simply competed with, and shouted over, the TV. Isaiah and Vivian refused to turn down the volume. They did that once a long time ago, and lost the sound. Isaiah beat the top of the set with his empty beer can, and miraculously, it came back on, loud. They felt they should not tempt fate by turning it down again. The straight backed, wooden chair between them often ended up piled with junk, food and paper overflow from the coffee table. I had to remove the pile and balance it on the coffee table before I could sit down between them during my visits. To hold a conversation, we waited for the lulls in the game show screaming, and stopped talking when the games' contestants and audiences became loud and excited. The living room also had a hard packed dirt floor, but it was covered by a cracked, donated linoleum that rolled out over the dirt, and held it down. The walls in this room were surprisingly intact, so no rain came through the cinder blocks in the living room. Donated lamps with dry rot shades on each of the end tables lighted the area, and made this room seem almost pleasant.

Isaiah was a semi-retired "yard and handy man." His hair was white-gray, short and woolly. He always had a few days growth of beard, but I never knew if he ever shaved, or even needed to. It always seemed to stay the same length. The families he had worked for over the years cared about him and Vivian. They gave him work when they could, even though it took Isaiah a long time to do it. They probably considered paying Isaiah as "charity." They remembered different times, times years ago, when he worked faster and better. Their loyalty to Isaiah and Vivian is what brought me to them. The families learned from Isaiah that Vivian had suffered a stroke, and was mostly paralyzed on the left side of her body. She dragged herself around her house somehow, but she wasn't able to do the domestic work she had done any more. The families didn't know what to do. They knew Isaiah could never support the both of them, so they called me to visit Vivian and Isaiah to see what could be done.

Someone had applied for SSI disability benefits for Vivian, perhaps someone from the hospital. Vivian didn't know and couldn't remember. She only knew that she would have to see a psychiatrist to see if her "problem" wasn't all in her head. Probably the government trying to save tax dollars, I thought, by telling Vivian that her "problem" was all in her head, and not due to having a cerebral aneurysm. Well, a cerebral aneurysm was in "her head" in a manner of speaking. Vivian had an appointment to see the disability board's designated psychiatrist next week, and needed a ride to get to him. I said I would take her if she could somehow manage to get in the front seat of my blue, two-door, Fairmont sedan. She said she would do it…not "could" do it, but "would" do it. The arrangements for the journey were made with the three of us shouting to each other over the loud "Price is Right" TV show. Both of them would go to Vivian's psychiatrist's meeting in my car. Isaiah said he should go to help Vivian. Vivian used a crutch on her good side, pulling along the rest of her. Isaiah said he would manage her bad side. It was arranged, and they bade me "Good-bye," Vivian with a wave from her good right arm, and Isaiah with a salute from his half filled beer can. I let myself out, and they quickly returned to the excitement as the wheel was spun on the "Price is Right."

I looked up at the sky. It was just as gray and full of cloudy disorder as was the inside of Vivian and Isaiah's cinderblock house. I got into my car just before a storm broke, and the rain really came down. Tomorrow, their kitchen would be wet, sloppy and slippery from this rain. Perhaps, after this disability situation was settled, I could help them move into another place….one with real floors, real floors in all the rooms. That was a goal for them, I thought as I backed out of the lumpy, rutted driveway to the gravel street, and then onto the paved boulevard. The windshield wipers beat rhythmically, sweeping clean the built-up dust and dirt from Isaiah and Vivian's gravel road, and the bumpy, root-filled yard. I returned to my office to make plans, and had a message waiting for me when I returned.

The disability board still wanted Vivian to see the psychiatrist, but said there was another problem. There was no proof of Vivian's date of birth or age. Vivian's mother, being poor and a field hand, had never thought about, or filed for a birth certificate. That was something White folks did. Field hands' children didn't need a birth certificate. After all, they were only going to grow up to be a field hand, or maybe, if they were lucky, a domestic in some fine White person's big house. Vivian's mother, who couldn't read or write, did have someone "scribe" Vivian's birth in the Bible. The scribe might have been the midwife who entered Vivian's birthday. Vivian's mother, while she couldn't read it, knew the Bible was the Bible, and she was proud that she owned one. It would have been very useful to have had that Bible. There was only one problem, though. Before Isaiah and Vivian moved to the cinderblock house, they had lived in a wooden two-room house with cardboard taped to the walls as insulation against the winter. One cold, rainy day, their fickle space heater sparked and caught the place on fire. The house burned to the ground. The hungry fire consumed clothing, furniture, dishes, aluminum cans, a television, cardboard insulation, magazine pictures taped to the walls as decorations, Isaiah's yard tools, and the one book they owned, the Bible. I would have to think of some other way to establish Vivian's birth date or age. Without proof of her age, the disability board would not pay a paralyzed Vivian disability checks. After all, rules are rules.

The next day, I returned to their home. I knocked and let myself in after they yelled to me from their chairs. I glanced to the right and to the left. The kitchen was muddy and impassible. The television blared "Jeopardy," but the living room was warm and puddle-less. I picked up the papers from the wooden visitor's chair and sat between them in it. I wondered and asked, "Vivian, do you remember where you lived during a census year?... 1930, 1940, 1950?" She thought a moment, stroked her lips with her useful, right, working hand, and then brightened, "Yes! Yes, I do!" "You do?" I was overwhelmed. "Yes, in 1930 I was six years old, and I was in the first grade in the colored country school. Two white people came by the school to take our names... said they were counting the people for the government. They took my name and all the other children's names and wrote it down in a big book." She smiled thinking of that day, "I liked school. I couldn't stay long though. Mother needed me in the fields, and she could only afford to send one of us to school. My brother went, and I went into the fields. I earned an extra quarter a day working with my Mother, and that was a big help in those days," she beamed. "Do you remember the address of the school?" I held no hopes that she would have that information. "Oh, yes," she said, and then proceeded to recite it to me, including the dates she attended the colored, country school. I was amazed. I asked if the elementary school had a name. She said, "No." It was only the colored, country school, and it wasn't an elementary school. It went up to the 8th Grade, period. It had one building, one room, and all the grades. She then went on to tell me that the teacher had one big, thick book. She started at the front of the book, and worked her way, student by student, to the end. The students had a few books that they could share, and everyone had a small, black slate and broken scrapes of chalk. When the student got to the end of the big book, school ended for him. Leaving school, the "graduated" student went to work as a field hand on farms, as a servant in White homes, as a handy man, as a helper to a merchant or tradesman, or they got married. Usually the marriage was between a young girl, 15 or so, to an older man whose wife had died and who needed help raising his children while he was working in the field. Vivian, of course, did not "graduate." She had had only six weeks of the first grade, but she was very proud of the fact that she had had six weeks of the first grade. Six weeks, the sum total of her formal education, six weeks. As we spoke further, I learned that her brother brought home all his lessons, and even a book from time to time. Whatever he learned in school that day, he "taught" Vivian that night. This is how Vivian learned to read, to write and to 'cipher figures. She worked sun-up to sundown with her mother in the fields, and after supper, she studied with her brother. When her brother finished "The Book," Vivian's education was finished as well. In the evenings, she did read the Bible to her mother who delighted in the words, and was so proud that her two children were "educated." The three of them worked the fields together. Five years later, a heavy piece of farm machinery fell on her mother, and she died. The Order of the Tents ladies washed her mother's body, laid it out on the kitchen table wrapped in a white sheet, sat with it during the wake, and oversaw the men of the community carry and bury her remains in a valley cemetery reserved for colored people. There were no colored funeral homes then out in the country. After the ceremony a few days later, Vivian took the Bible and went to work in the home of the General Store's owner. Her brother stayed in the house, and worked in the farmer's fields until his health and spirit broke down and he died. By and by, Vivian met Isaiah, who also worked for the store owner. Isaiah and Vivian became a couple and moved in together. They never had children, just kept on with their jobs and moved from one cheap rented house to another cheap, rented house. Sometimes a White man who owned a cheap, rented house would give them a discount. The wooden house with the cardboard "insulation," that burned down, for instance, was $40 a month. They felt lucky to find such a bargain. It burned down, of course. It probably should have been torn down, but they felt lucky to have a White man who would give them a place to stay at a bargain.

The day for the medical assessment by the psychiatrist arrived. Getting Vivian from the house to the car and into the car, plus the journey from their home to the office took longer than the actual visit itself. Vivian hadn't been in the doctor's office more than seven minutes when the doctor came out of the examining room to find me. "Why am I seeing Vivian?" he asked. "She was sent by the disability board for this evaluation." I explained, "They said her disability is all in her head." "This woman has had a major stroke that has rendered her left side paralyzed." He responded, "Are they crazy at the disability board? Where are the papers?" I handed them to him. "We'll just put this right, and right now." He turned and disappeared into a separate office. I could hear him dialing the telephone and then yelling into the receiver. It was loud and muffled, but I did understand and heard the words "stupid," "crazy" and "a waste of my time." I sat back in the waiting room while he made entries on the official assessment forms. When he was done, he escorted Vivian and Isaiah out to the waiting room. He put his arm lightly around Vivian's shoulders, "Miss Vivian, it is going to be all right. You will get your disability check soon. Don't you worry." He shook Isaiah's hand and told him to take good care of Vivian. We three left, and as I glanced over my shoulder to look at the psychiatrist, I saw him shake his head, turn and enter one of his other examining rooms. Hopefully, there was a real patient in there who needed his help.

Two months later, and after her final appeal before the Administrative Law Judge, (ALJ), the psychiatrist's educated prophesy came true. Vivian asked me to represent her at the hearing, and I did. I reminded the ALJ that Vivian was no longer able to work in the field in which she had been trained, as a domestic, and that her disability was indeed expected to last at least one year. The ALJ agreed, and Vivian received her first disability check as well as a letter stating she would soon receive a lump sum, retroactive check from the time of her initial application to the month of her first "official" disability check. This was good news. Vivian also received her Medicare card so she could select and see a doctor of her choice.

In the two months we waited for the official disability determination, we worked together on improving the house. Isaiah was content in the house, and didn't want to move. Vivian didn't feel she had the strength to move. Their landlord had given them a "discount" in the rent when Vivian could no longer work, but the landlord refused to make any improvements. He said he'd have to raise the rent if he did, but, "wonderful man" that he was, he agreed to let me bring in an agency that made home repairs for low-income renters, and not raise the rent. The agency used shovels to lift the dirt and debris by the pounds into dark green plastic bags. They threw out bags of donated clothes that were ruined from water and mold, or simply smelled bad. They sealed and painted the walls against rain; installed a real floor over the dirt throughout the house; put in a new, larger and more efficient space heater; cleaned, painted and secured the kitchen cabinets; cleaned and caulked windows and slip covered the furniture.

I contacted a group of ladies from the Methodist Church who volunteered to put up new curtains at the windows, and to stock the pantry with shelf-stable foods and paper goods. The ladies promised to come on a regular basis to wash and rehang the curtains, to "tidy up," and to replenish the pantry stock. They also dragged Isaiah's tall, full, clear plastic bags of beer cans to a less obvious location between two bushes behind the house. They replaced the beer can bags with two pots of flowers at the front door. I'm not sure that Isaiah liked having his collections out of his sight, but he suffered it so long as no one else could see them and take them away. There was something about old time Methodist ladies not liking to have tall clear plastic bags of beer cans in general view, especially on either side of the front door.

As Isaiah and Vivian's financial and environmental circumstances improved, I had the leisure to really observe and focus on their unique "communication skills," and marital "rules of engagement." They obviously cared for each other, and each was faithful to the other and had been for years and years. But, like any couple, there were moments of disagreement and differences of opinion, especially over money and the amounts of money spent on beer. One day while I sat in my usual spot between them on the wooden chair in the living room, Vivian, during a lull in "Let's Make A Deal," when the contestant was deciding on "box # 1" or a new refrigerator, said, "Isaiah, tell Missy here about your FOUR bags of beer cans!" She looked at me in a knowing way and said, "Those sweet ladies you got us told me that Isaiah has FOUR bags and not two. They thought someone else was helpin' him collect the cans." Isaiah protested, waggin' his head around with his eyes half closed, "Naw, naw, woman. You gots no right to tell Missy about my beer cans. She knows all 'bout it." Vivian kept at him, "Missy also knows we have more money now, and YOU'RE spendin' it." She paused, " 'Fess up, 'Saiah! 'Fess up and tell Missy that you been buying LOTS more beer!" Isaiah's face looked grim. He glared into Vivian's eyes, completely forgetting that I was sitting between them. "I tol' you woman, you gots NO right to tell Missy 'bout my beer. I'm about to teach you some lessons of manners.

Remember, I am the man! I am the boss!" Isaiah was somewhat unsteady as he rose from his chair still glaring into her eyes. He squinted and started to take a shuffling step toward her. I was sure someone was about to suffer bodily harm, perhaps even me! Vivian frowned and glared back at Isaiah. She would not be moved. She squinted her eyes, and set her lips determinedly. Isaiah took another shuffling step toward her. Vivian was not afraid. I was afraid, but Vivian was not afraid. Vivian stared straight into Isaiah's eyes. Isaiah staggered a bit. Vivian reached behind her to the table beside her, on her good right side. Faster than I could say, "Wow!" Vivian had a long, sharp pair of paper scissors firmly grasped in her good hand, raised high over her head and aimed directly at Isaiah. Isaiah's gaze shifted from Vivian's eyes to the long pair of scissors aimed at him. He stopped shuffling toward Vivian. His eyes opened wider, but he did not gasp or shout. He simply huffed, turned slightly and plopped back down in his chair. Once he was settled, Vivian put down her scissors, but still glared at him. "Woman, you SHAME me in front of Missy!" he said. He rubbed his brow, put his hands on the arms of the chair and started to rise again. As he did, Vivian raised her scissors. He sat down the second time, and heaved a heavy sigh. He was not going to prevail in this discussion. He sat and focused his attention on "Let's Make A Deal." The contestant had chosen the box over the refrigerator and had won two live pigs that came squealing out of the box. Each had a ribbon around its neck. The audience went wild and the contestant, dressed as Minnie Mouse, covered her face with her big gloves and shook her head. Vivian looked at the show, muttered "Dummy, should have taken the refrigerator. What is she going to do with two pigs?" Isaiah said, "You're right, Vivian. She should a taken the refrigerator." They were both fine and back to normal. Everything was forgotten and forgiven, but the scissors were still on the right side of Vivian, just in case. I was shaken, but apparently this scenario happened from time to time. This was how their differences were resolved, and it worked for them. No marital counseling. No role-playing. No nothing. Isaiah gets up mad. Vivian picks up the scissors. Isaiah sits down. Vivian puts down the scissors. Isaiah gets mad and stands up again. Vivian picks up the scissors. Those were the rules, and it worked, for them.

I stayed with their case for a few more years. Isaiah, who had his proof of age, eventually became old enough to draw an SSI pension. With Vivian's disability check and Isaiah's check, they were able to make it. They even bought a new, used TV, color, and with a volume control. After a few years, the landlord decided he could get more rent on his improved property so he evicted them. Being evicted can sometimes be a good thing. Evicted Senior Citizens go to the top of the list for subsidized Senior Housing. Within a month of the landlord's action, I was able to settle them into a Senior Housing apartment. The apartment had it all, heat, air-conditioning, carpet, a working kitchen, a full bathroom and neighbors. Vivian and Isaiah stayed mainly to themselves, but there were neighbors if they wanted them. The Methodist ladies went shopping for them, food, not beer. Isaiah aged and cut down on his beer anyway. He did find a neighbor, though, who would go shopping for him for beer, so he still managed to collect twelve to twenty-four cans a month. Not too bad. The scissors stayed within reach of Vivian's right hand, although she didn't seem to have much need for them any more. Time passed, and Vivian had another major stroke that took her away. Isaiah lasted a few months more, and then he followed her. They were buried in the old "colored cemetery" in the country next to Vivian's mother and brother. There were no survivors. The families who had employed Isaiah, the Methodist ladies, the visiting nurse and I, were the only mourners at each ceremony. We donated their things to other seniors in need. The visiting nurse distributed all but one of their things. I wanted the scissors. Everyone said it would be "OK" to keep them, so I did. I keep them on my desk. They are very sharp and useful, and I think of Vivian and Isaiah every time I see them.

KATIE

Katie had given birth to eight children, yet when her doctor asked the standard OB/GYN question, "Are you a virgin?" she always answered, "Yes." He said, "But Katie, you have eight children!" To which she would reply, "I'm not responsible for what I do in my sleep." Katie had a keen sense of humor, and, given her life's circumstances, she needed it.

Katie's late husband was a bread man. In those days, bread men delivered a truck load of white and wheat bread, rolls, cakes, coffee cakes, bagels, English muffins, cupcakes, and French and Italian long loaves to grocery stores and schools throughout a four city area. Everything was baked the night before, and the bread man loaded up his truck around 3:00 a.m. to assure delivery of fresh products. The bread man had to be careful that none of the products was crushed or damaged, but things happen when you are dealing with a truckload of baked goods. Imperfect products were supposed to be discarded, but rather than throw them in the trash, Katie's husband would bring the crushed loaves and ripped packages home. Ten hungry people were not that particular about the condition of a loaf of bread or package of pastries. "One" and "Two Day Old" products were also available to the bread men for consumption or destruction. Bruised and old products were part of the benefit package for bread men to take home to their families.

When he died at age 61, Katie was left plump, penniless and worried. Bread men had no pension for themselves or their wives. Katie was 59, too young for a Social Security widow's benefit, and there were no savings or investments to sustain her. The house was paid for, but that was it. No money for utilities, food or medicine. Luckily, two of the eight adult children needed a home and came to live with her; one unmarried son, also a bread man, and a divorced daughter with two school-age children. Katie enjoyed their company, and her house was once more filled with people, and a lot of day-old bread and rolls.

Her son, Arnold, was the last of her adult children; a smiling, cheerful yet simple young man, and a bread man like his father. He never married, or even dated, afraid of girls or possibly too shy. Driving the bread truck and bringing home baked products, just like his father, was purpose enough in life for him. Whenever the social worker came to speak with his mother, he leaned up against the wall behind her, folded his arms across his chest and smiled the sweet smile of a slow person afraid to enter into the conversation, but fascinated by the exchanges between his mother and the social worker. Both the ladies had good senses of humor, and both ladies enjoyed bantering with each other. Sometimes his brow would knit as if to say, "How can they come up with all those funny things so fast?"

Phyllis, Katie's daughter, was thin, blonde, smart, and jobless. Her two children attended the elementary school a few blocks away. Both of them were subject to respiratory infections, so both of them were home a lot. Their father sent support payments when it suited him, fairly regularly, but not always on time. Phyllis tried little part time jobs, but they didn't seem to last or amount to anything better. The children's illnesses, and her need for weekend, male companionship pretty much put an end to her "career ladder" before it had really begun. Consequently, she applied for and received state aid payments, food stamps and medical assistance. She and the children had their own welfare social worker, and sometimes the home visit by the welfare worker would overlap with the visit from Katie's social worker. Arnold listened in on these conversations as well. The welfare worker arrived in the official city car, asked the same, prescribed questions each time from the official forms on her clipboard. She had no sense of humor, and her required visits were completed within twenty minutes to half an hour. Phyllis breathed a sigh of relief when she finished and drove away. Phyllis had answered the questions to the welfare worker's satisfaction, and she and her children would be left alone for another month. The welfare worker had the power to change or cut off any of the benefits the three of them received, they depended on all of them, so her visits were indeed stressful on Phyllis.

Katie's social worker helped her apply for and receive her widow's benefit at age 60, food stamps and medical assistance. While she did have diabetes, she was technically not "disabled" so could not receive any disability payments. Her widow's benefit wasn't much, but every little bit helped. Katie began to lose her sight from the diabetes. She was also losing the feeling in her feet from the disease, so walking was a problem. Katie had one passion, aside from humor and making people laugh. She loved to crochet. Katie made doll clothes for her grand daughter. She made afghans, table runners, tablecloths, bedspreads, and sweaters. It was beginning to bother her about losing her sight, so she practiced crocheting by feel, creating a Braille system for herself to create beautiful things. Katie used most of her widow's pension to buy yarn for her projects. It was her other purpose in life.

The three adults pooled their money to keep the lights and heat on. Food stamps brought in food not donated by the bread company. The food stamp food was never enough for all of them, and the end of the month was pretty lean, food wise. Bread and baked products, old or damaged, was what mostly filled up the four of them. Not good for Katie's diabetes or the children's frequent infections, but that was the way it was. Katie's social worker would surprise them with a grocery bag of food from a church's food closet, but Katie was proud and told her that she wished she hadn't brought it. "Give it to someone really in need," Katie would say.

Arnold and Katie had once been keen on planting a garden in the stony back yard, but the squirrels and the rabbits ate most of what tried to come up between the rocks; and with Arnold away most of the day or sleeping, and Katie not able to half see, they gave up on the idea of a vegetable garden. They simply made do with what they had until one month when a financial emergency took what little extra they had saved. A severe water leak meant paying the plumber, and buying a new water heater. This expense meant not paying the electric bill. The next month, a new battery was needed for the old car Phyllis used to take the children to the clinic and to go to the grocery store. That meant not paying the electric bill. The power company sent a turn-off notice. The autumn weather had turned from balmy warm to cold. They couldn't let the power be turned off. Phyllis told her ex-husband. He didn't care for her anymore, but he did care for his children. He gave her $75 in cash to pay the power company, which she did. The lights and heat stayed on.

Phyllis knew she would have to tell the welfare worker about the cash from the children's father, but she didn't. The welfare worker never knew until two or three months had passed and Phyllis' conscience got the better of her. She "confessed" to the welfare worker on one of the monthly visits, and showed her the receipt for the $75 payment to keep the power on. The welfare worker made a bad face and said that $75 dollars would have to be paid to the Welfare office to make books balance. It was considered "excess and unreported income." Phyllis said she would do this, somehow. The family pooled money from their combined incomes, ate more bread and paid the Welfare office the "excess and unreported" $75. Phyllis thought everything was all right. The next month the welfare worker said another $75 in fines was to be paid to the Welfare office for the illegal act of accepting "income" from a previously unreported source. The family pooled money from their combined incomes, again, ate more bread and paid the Welfare office an additional $75. Phyllis thought everything was all right. The third month the welfare worker stated an additional fine was needed to make full restitution for Phyllis' misdeed. The family pooled money from their combined incomes, a third time, ate more bread and paid the Welfare office an additional $75. Phyllis thought surely now everything was all right, and it was, for the next six months. The family had repaid the illegally received $75 three times over. That should surely be enough they thought, but it wasn't.

The commonwealth's Attorney learned of Phyllis' misdeed and felt, according to the "letter of the law", this was welfare fraud and should be punished to the maximum. A sheriff's deputy came to the door with a warrant for Phyllis' arrest. The adults and the children were hysterical as she was led away with her hands handcuffed behind her back. Katie and the children screamed as the Sheriff's deputy put his hand on Phyllis' head to guide her into the back seat of the vehicle. Neighbors came out, watched and pointed as the squad car drove away. Phyllis was processed and locked up. There was no money for bail. None of the other adult children would help. They felt Phyllis had "made her bed" and now "she could lie in it." The month she was incarcerated, the welfare payments stopped. The family ate more bread brought by the other drivers who would normally take the bruised loaves home to their families. Her case was scheduled on the court docket one month after her arrest. A court appointed attorney was given to her. He saw Phyllis two days before court to prepare himself to defend her. Phyllis had asked Katie's social worker to come as a character witness for her, to talk about Phyllis giving Katie her insulin shots, preparing the meals, caring for her sickly children and keeping house. The social worker agreed to do this.

The prosecuting attorney was aggressive in painting a picture of Phyllis as a welfare fraud "queen," and wanted the maximum sentence allowable. It was later learned that this attorney had her eyes set on the Commonwealth Attorney's position at the next election when the Commonwealth Attorney was set to run for Attorney General. Punishing welfare fraud would look good on her resume come November. The testimony from Katie's social worker was arbitrarily dismissed saying, "Anyone could be trained to do what Phyllis did, even the older of the two children (13), or the brother. This welfare fraud MUST be punished to the maximum as an example to all the other recipients." And punished she was. Phyllis was sentenced to three months in jail, and then was placed on supervised probation for six months PROVIDED she could find a job. Otherwise, it was nine months in jail. Katie's social worker contacted one of Phyllis' other brothers, one who had an accounting business, and pleaded with him to please help Phyllis, for Katie's sake. It took him a long time to come to a decision, but he finally did. He agreed to let Phyllis have a job as the janitor for six months, but no longer. Phyllis was grateful, and Katie was grateful, but neither ever learned the full extent of Katie's social worker's intervention on Phyllis' behalf.

After nine months, the ordeal was over. Phyllis found a real job, left welfare and cut down on her weekend trips with male friends. She worked at a convenience store near the home, and soon was made the night manager. The family continued to pool their resources and things were pretty "normal" for the next year. Katie's social worker continued to help Katie with whatever programs or benefits she could find. Katie seemed content, and brightened up anytime her social worker arrived and they could joke and banter. The diabetes was increasing its hold on her, and not only taking her vision and destroying her kidneys, but giving her vivid and frightening dreams of persons long dead coming up the stairs to "get her." Her only salvation and respite from these dreams was in her crocheting. She was determined to make an afghan of many bright colors for her social worker. These bright colors were easier for her to "see," and the yarn was left over from other projects. The social worker protested, but Katie said that if she didn't accept it as a gift of love, she, Katie, would never let the social worker in her home again. Well, that settled it. Katie worked on the afghan for over two months. It had to be perfect, she said, so she pulled out sections that were not perfect to her, and worked them again. It gave her so much pleasure to create this afghan of many colors, that she had no frightening dreams during this period. The vivid and recurring dreams of her husband, covered in blood, coming into her room to grab her by the foot and tell her it was time to die and to come with him to the other side stopped completely. Katie was so very proud of the afghan. It was a happy afghan. It had thick and thin stripes of red, blue, white, yellow, green, purple and orange, bright clean colors; and Katie was so very happy in making it.

When it was ready, Katie wrapped the "perfect" afghan in pale blue tissue paper, and tied it with a gold cord. There it was, a gift of love for her friend, her social worker, her comrade in joke-telling and pun-making. She wanted it to be perfect and it was. The social worker was still hesitant to accept it. The agency had rules about accepting gifts from clients over a dollar level of $10, but when she saw the look of great happiness on Katie's face as she presented the package to her with outstretched arms, she thought to herself, this means so much to Katie, to refuse it would be a slap in the face to Katie, and, perhaps, because it was made up of left-over yarn, it might be within the $10 gift threshold. She untied the thin, gold cord, and peeled back the pale blue tissue paper, and unfolded the glorious afghan. She held it high to take in all the colors. Katie clapped her hands in excitement. She was finally able to GIVE instead of RECEIVE. This made her especially happy. The social worker was very pleased with her gift. It would be her "happy quilt," she told Katie. Whenever she felt down in the dumps, she would wrap herself in it, think of Katie's kindness and generosity to her, and "cheer up" knowing she had such a good friend as Katie. This pleased Katie no end. It indeed was a happy day.

The day of the "happy quilt" marked the fourth anniversary of the social worker visiting and assisting Katie. Katie was progressively declining in health. Her legs now retained significant fluid, and this was coupled with the lack of feeling in her feet. Infections were a prime cause of worry, as they may not heal and could lead to amputation. Katie mainly stayed in her wheelchair, listened to the television, crocheting and chatting with any visitors or family members who happened by. A month or so after the "happy quilt" day, Katie called the social worker in a panic. She breathlessly told her the dreams had returned. Her husband came for her every night, and she was afraid to fall asleep. She had gone to the doctor for medicine, some to hopefully ease the fluid that had gotten her legs so tight that she felt as though they would split, and a mild sleeping pill to get her through the night. All the sleeping pill seemed to do, though, was to keep her a prisoner in the nightmare, terrified, and unable to wake up from its horror. She told the social worker she stopped taking the sleeping pill. With no sleeping pill, she could wake up from the devastating dreams to escape them. The doctor said her heart was becoming weaker and weaker. She was not a candidate for any invasive course of treatment, and it was only a matter of time for her. The social worker visited more frequently and tried to calm Katie. The minister from a church that Katie had attended many years ago was called to visit. They talked about the church. Katie said she always felt at peace there. The stained glass windows were so beautiful that the very remembrance of the sun shining through them brought tears to her eyes. She could no longer see, except in her imagination or in the dreams. The minister calmed her and did bring an element of peace and tranquility to her. He told her to focus on her faith, her memories of the church and to put her life in God's hands. He told her a special Guardian Angel was with her and would not let the terrors of the night dreams harm her. Katie drew strength from his words. He was right. She had no more bloody dreams. Her only dreams were filled with sunlight and clouds and angels and a far away bright light that seemed to come closer to her each time she dreamed the dream. At the end, she told the social worker she thought she almost saw

God hovering within that bright orb. It didn't frighten her, it soothed her, and she welcomed it each night.

Three months after the minister's visit Katie fell asleep and did not wake up. Phyllis looked in on her and saw her smiling. She thought Katie was sleeping. When Katie didn't wake up at her usual time, or an hour later, Phyllis went in, rubbed her arm to rouse her, and learned the truth. Katie was gone. Phyllis covered her mouth and sobbed. Her shoulders heaved and her crying became louder. Arnold ran into the room. Her children looked in from the door holding onto the doorframe. Soon all four were crying and wailing in unison, hugging each other and kneeling by Katie's bed. It was over. Their mother and grandmother was gone.

The social worker attended Katie's small funeral. The minister saw to it that Katie was buried in the church cemetery near and under the stained glass window. She would always be near that place that had given her so much comfort and joy in life. Katie would have liked that.

Katie's "happy quilt" was just that. Whenever the social worker felt she had too much on her, whenever frustrations and worries piled on her, she wrapped herself in Katie's "happy quilt," thought of Katie, and her world was indeed a better place. "Thank you, Katie," she thought, "Thank you."

WILLIE

Willie was the only man I have ever known who was a truck farmer, lived on three acres of land in the country, farmed rented land, and had wall-to-wall, white, spotless carpets in his home. He was an immaculate house and yard keeper. Every bush on the three landscaped acres was pruned to a shape. Some were ball shaped, some triangles like Christmas trees, some rectangles and some were squares. Each of them was perfect. Willie did everything himself. The grass was cut to never be higher than one inch. The gravel drive showed no growth of grass or weeds. The lawn had no stray pieces of gravel flung on it by the arriving or departing cars and trucks. The house itself even had white, upholstered furniture, done over by his late wife. Both Willie and his wife were meticulous. The furniture was over ten years old, but looked showroom new, and professionally manufactured. The kitchen had only one coffee pot on the long L-shaped, expansive counter. No dirty dishes were ever stacked in the sink, or even in the dish drainer. The vinyl floor was mopped and buffed everyday. The few knick-knacks he had were placed within an oak, antique curio cabinet with curved, glass doors and thick, glass shelves. Dust was nowhere to be found in Willie's house, not even within the oak curio cabinet. I have never known anyone, man or woman, to keep such a house and yard, but Willie did. When I would arrive to help him, Willie would always apologize for not having the house absolutely perfect, whatever that was. He apologized as he had been working out in the field and tending the vegetables for most of the day. I saw nothing wrong. It looked "perfect" to me, but then, I wasn't Willie.

Willie's grown son was tall, trim, smart and a "dandy" man. He fancied himself a gift from God to all ladies, even though he had a good job and a wife. He always seemed to need money for "things." Willie showed me the racks of suits and slacks and sports coats hung and arranged by color in the second bedroom. Each piece was cloaked in clear plastic and waiting for the "dandy" man. Willie's son borrowed money from what little Willie had from his Social Security. He felt he needed a super sports car, so he got one. For extra money, he had Willie sign for a second and third mortgage to fund his extravagances. When the "Willie well" dried up, the son began stealing from this employer. His employer soon discovered the embezzlement, and when confronted, the son skipped. Eventually the police found him in the next state, and he was extradited to stand trial. He was tried, convicted and sentenced to a number of years in prison, hence the clothes waiting for him in the second bedroom. Willie saw his son every few months. His son couldn't take any more from Willie, and Willie knew where the son was. Willie was comfortable with that arrangement. His son's wife even visited him, but none of his lady friends. These were good things for Willie, but the second and third mortgages were still there, unpaid, and events were beginning to come to a head. The bank wanted to sell Willie's property, and, by law, they were entitled to do so.

Willie had a good friend of many years, an old lawyer in town. The lawyer was from an longtime, powerful country family that ran most everything in the small town. The lawyer hired Willie to keep the yard at his office and at his home as pristine as Willie kept his own yards. The lawyer learned about Willie's troubles when Willie brought some legal looking papers in a thick manila envelope to him to decipher. Willie could not read. He was totally illiterate, and never understood what he was signing with his "X."

He knew that this packet was important, but never realized just how important. It was simply so much bigger than anything he's ever received, and by the weight of it, it seemed important.

The lawyer, after reading the contents and making some calls to the bank, talking to his school chum, the Bank President, called me in to help with whatever programs and benefits I could find for Willie. He promised Willie and me to keep the title to the property somewhat "clouded" so no clear sale could easily take place. We communicated with each other and worked as a team to keep Willie in his home and on his land as long as possible.

This seemed to satisfy Willie. He had no comprehension of the severity of the package, but as long as the lawyer smiled at him and told him it would be all right, and to go home and be about his business, he was satisfied. The bank put a "For Sale" sign on the property. This did worry Willie. He could not read the sign, but he figured out what it was. He had seen them before, seen the old owner leave and seen the new owner come in. When he was worried, he would call either the lawyer or me. We told him that we were working to let him finish his years out on his property. Willie was 85, and the lawyer and I thought this was reasonable. Willie knew that whenever someone came by the property to ask about the price and all that, he was to immediately call either the lawyer or me. If me, I had a standard answer, "The title is clouded, and the sale will be difficult." If the lawyer, it was a similar remark, but cast in legalese. The potential buyer then went on his way to shop for another country property. In a way it was Willie's fault that so many people stopped. The property was immaculate...almost a Hollywood set. Buyers were simply drawn to it in all its pristine beauty. Companion properties in Willie's neighborhood had overgrown yards, rusty farm implements stacked and parked on the side and back yards, and paint peeling and roofs patched with a variety of colored shingles. Dogs ran wild on other properties, peed on bushes and turned them yellow. An old, confused neighbor lady said someone had come by and set fire to her unkempt yellow bushes. She never did get the connection between the roaming dogs and her yellow bushes. Willie's, by contrast, were dark green and shiny. He even washed his bushes between rainstorms. He yelled at the dogs and fired birdshot over their heads. They left his yard and bushes alone.

Every few months Willie would visit his younger sister, his only other relative, in the next town. He could drive himself in his old pickup truck. He had a driver's license. He couldn't read or write, but he took the test verbally. He knew the color and shapes of the signs, "stop," "yield," and "railroad crossing," etc., and he could match the speed limit sign to the numbers on his odometer. I asked him how he managed to get from the country to his sister's home fifteen miles away. It was simple, he told me, and he rattled off all the landmarks he used for turns and distance markers. He used a barn, a gas station, a traffic light, traffic arrows on the road, a gun shop, a grocery store, and all the other landmarks that guided his trail. In a way, he was better than me trying to navigate using my map and watch for addresses and street signs. He always got to his sister's safely, and back home to the country with no problem. He was worried about her. The doctors said she had cancer and it was serious. His sister was younger than Willie, had gone to school and had learned to read. She knew she was in for a difficult time, and wanted Willie to be with her as much as possible. Her husband had died in an automobile accident ten years before, and her only child, a son was away in the military. Willie was her only "family" close by. She was scared, and she needed him. For this reason, Willie tried to visit her at least once a month.

One, two…five years passed. His sister had her good days and painful days. Chemotherapy and radiation squeezed out as many extra months and years as possible. Her doctors had no explanation for her extended life, and no prognosis for her future here on earth. It was a day-to-day thing.

The lawyer and I had grown very skillful in fending off would-be buyers for Willie's property. The bank President suffered his loss for these five years at the behest of, and on account of his friendship with the lawyer, but as all good things must come to an end, so did Willie's "grace period" on his property. The President contacted the Sheriff to post a sign stating that in six months an auction of Willie's property would be held on the courthouse steps. It would then be real. Willie would have to leave.

The lawyer had me bring Willie into his office to discuss the implications and impact the Sheriff's auction would on Willie's well-ordered life. At first Willie said nothing, then he cried. He put his head in his hands and cried tears of loss, sadness and despair. Maybe there was some mistake? Maybe the bank would let him live out there just a little longer? Couldn't the lawyer talk with his friend the President and do this little thing for Willie? The lawyer said he had "pulled all the rabbits out of the hat" that he could over the past five years, and the property would be sold in six months at the Sheriff's auction. Willie cried and wailed again. It was so painful to sit there and hear him. He was losing everything, everything. I patted his back and shoulder. He put his head in my lap and continued to sob. I rubbed his back. The lawyer was silent. By and by, Willie came to himself. He sniffed and sat up, took out his red, bandana handkerchief and blew his nose. It stayed quiet. Willie spoke first, "What do I do now?" The lawyer told him to remove all his personal effects, furniture, linens, dishes, shoes, clothing, knick-knacks, pots and pans and store them, give them away or sell them. The house should be empty, totally, two weeks before the sale. Willie said there was a lot of stuff, but he would do it. As I drove Willie home, he cried a little, but was sitting up straight with a determined look on his face as we pulled into the drive and the wheels crunched the gravel. He looked around at his property and pointed at the three bushes beside his back door. "I'll have to trim those three fellows tonight. It's going to rain, and they'll start growing by tomorrow." He didn't mention anything more about our meeting with the lawyer, but thanked me for the ride into town and hopped out of my car. Pretty spry for an almost 90-year-old man, I thought. I didn't mention anything about the meeting either. I was just glad that I had driven. It would have been hard for him to drive, what with his crying and all. I wished him a good evening, and said I would call him later in the week. He tipped his hat to me, and went to his shed for his clippers. Sure enough, later that evening, just about the time Willie would have finished trimming the three bushes, it poured down in the buckets. The sky was crying for Willie, too.

When I next spoke with Willie, he was calm and his voice had a hint of happiness in it. He had spoken to his sister and told her all about his losing his property. Instead of commiserating with him and saying, "Oh how sad" and things like that, she was elated and excited. She said, "Now Willie, you can come to live with me. We'll help each other. You can put all your things in my garage or in my house, whatever you want. You just bring them out here and we'll figure it out. Oh, Willie, I am so happy." Willie was surprised and completely taken aback. He'd never thought of that, hadn't even given it a passing thought. He was so involved with his loss, he never even fathomed another possibility.

"Well, Willie, it looks like you and your sister have a plan, and it sounds like a good one," I said to him. "Yes, ma'm, I am starting today to haul things to her place. My church members said they'd help me load and unload. I've got five and a half months to do it, and it will get done." He was so happy. He had a purpose and he had hope. I guess when a "door closes," a "window opens," or so they say.

Willie took his time and moved everything into his sister's place. He even had time to trim the bushes and mow the lawns before he left. He backed out of the drive, stopped and looked around one last time...not really in sadness, but to see if he had done a good enough job. He wanted to leave it right. He wanted to leave it perfect, and he did.

The bidders at the Sheriff's auction were amazed at the beauty of the property, and the cleanliness of the house. Surely a single man didn't just live here alone? "Oh, yes," the Sheriff assured them, "Willie is one of a kind!" The bidders shook their heads in disbelief. One raised his hand and said he had a question. "Sure," said the Sheriff. "Well, the house is completely empty, and we expected that, but upstairs in the second bedroom there are racks of men's clothes...suits, slacks, sports coats, shirts, belts, ties and at least twenty pairs of men's shoes lined up in the closet. Did Willie forget to take his clothes?" "Oh, no," said the

Sheriff who knew the whole story, "they go with the house. Whoever buys the house, gets the clothes too...no extra charge."

And with that, the bidding began. Willie's property had a new owner, the bank got its mortgage money, and Willie did not ever have to be reminded of his son in prison, and what he had done to him.

CONCLUSION

Our culture champions and promotes "Youth." Looking, staying and acting young are the goals of media, advertising and a compliant population. "Old" is dreary, sad and well, "old." Take a little time, however, and listen to the old.

The people in these stories lived their lives in times of great personal challenge. They traveled their "journey-road," and survived. They were strong, and didn't even really know they were strong. They cloaked themselves in a mantle of purpose, self-reliance and values as they traveled through the many years on their journey road. Making themselves rich, living a life only for the approval of others, or giving excuses for what befell them was not in their make up. Each kept true to his or her code of personal worth and ethics. This is what drove them, this is what sustained them in the most trying of times, and this is how they survived.

I was fortunate to have worked with older people during a time when the person, the client came first. We invested time with the person, as much time as was needed. Current "best practices" from human services and social services agencies stress "productivity" and "efficiency." The encouraged directive is to visit, screen assess and create a "care plan" in 45 minutes or less, then get onto the next client. In these 45 minutes, the old person has barely had enough time to recite his name, address, doctor(s), prescription medicines and functional daily living abilities. In 45 minutes there is little time to establish rapport or develop trust between the old person and the interviewer. And, there certainly is no time to tell the stories that makes that old person human, unique and a survivor. Certainly, the caseworker is there to

99

assist the old person with some services or programs, but the old person now needing support did not live to be 80, 90, or 110 by doing everything "wrong."

Take a little time. Listen to the old. You just might learn something.